C000081304

Life's Whispers:

Journeys to the Hospice

LOVE RAY
XXX

LIFE'S WHISPERS: JOURNEYS TO THE HOSPICE
Victoria Villaseñor and Nicci Robinson, Editors
Global Words Press
Copyright retained by individual authors
Cover design by Nicci Robinson
Internal Artwork by Buster Fisher
Collection copyright © 2018 Global Words Press
Imprint Digital, UK
Cataloging information
ISBN: 978-1-911227-14-4

LIFE'S WHISPERS:

JOURNEYS TO THE HOSPICE

2018
GLOBAL WORDS PRESS
NOTTINGHAM, UK

Preface

We went into this project as we go into all of our projects: with open hearts and minds. The people we were privileged to work with reached into our chests and opened our hearts still further. These projects invariably focus on the clients or service users of the charity, but this one was different. This one saw us delivering two sets of workshops because the interest was so phenomenally high, and it also saw both the staff and service users coming together to share their stories. And they shared them in the most fantastic and supportive environment we've ever come across. The interest and buy-in from everyone was amazing, and the personal experiences each of them offered up to share were extraordinarily varied.

These projects are about life writing, and the service users at the Nottinghamshire Hospice are acutely aware of the value of life. And yet still, they had the courage to dig deep, to remember, and to connect with some of their darkest times but also some of their most treasured memories. In looking back at their lives, it galvanised their connections with everyone else taking part in the project. It brought them together and gave them the strength to share their stories with us.

We're honoured to have been entrusted with those memories, and we hope you'll enjoy reading them.

Nicci Robinson and Victoria Villaseñor,
Directors, Global Wordsmiths

Foreword

It's a great pleasure to be asked to write the introduction to this collection of short stories. They are all different but spring from the same source, a space and time created at Nottinghamshire Hospice by Nicci Robinson and Victoria Villaseñor from Global Wordsmiths.

Eleven wonderful workshops were held, and those taking part went on a shared journey answering the question which challenges us all no matter who or where we are: "What's My Story?" There are many clichés which are often used when someone speaks about their expectations of what the end of life will be like. On this journey, all of the writers were able to use the space to write about what was important to them, what made them special, and what would be the legacy they placed in this book.

This explains why, when this opportunity from Global Wordsmiths was offered, we had no hesitation that something special would happen. Here at the Hospice our work is to "add life to days" for people whose life has been shortened by terminal, life-limiting illness. So much of our work is about understanding the stories of our patients, volunteers, and staff, and valuing and learning from each other. I hope by reading this book you too will add something to your day; insight, compassion, or a great big, hearty guffaw!

I congratulate all those involved and, from all of us, say thank you to Global Wordsmiths and the Arts Council for creating this amazing experience for us all here at Nottinghamshire Hospice.

Rowena Naylor-Morrell,
Chief Executive Officer

CONTENTS

Eye of the Beholder Chloe Edwards   1

Party Night Margaret White   17

From West Country to Up Country Brian T. Munson   21

The Kitten Betty Scott   31

The Greatest Prize of All Tessa Marie   35

A Memory Walk Kerry Lovell   39

The Road to Apathy... Joe McClaine   45

A Baby and A Flood Phyllis Betts   49

It's My Life Tina Barnes   53

Our Journey: My Letter to Tina Heather Barnes   65

Being a Longhorn Ron Gascoigne   77

My Life's Journey to Recovery Malcolm Corbett   81

Memories of a Broxtowe Boy Gordon West   87

Dreaming Yvonne Dunning   91

Saturday Night Out... Margaret Parkes   111

The Day My Life Began Raymond Mellors   115

Little Boy Jacob Lee   121

Traffic Lights Janice Dent   125

Dedication

For Jean,

Our lovely friend who started this
book with us, but unfortunately
didn't make it to the end of our journey.

Eye of the Beholder
Chloe Edwards

Hot, noisy steam was erupting from behind the counter. A long queue of exhausted shoppers, all jostling to see the array of extravagant lattes and mochas. All of them impatient to get their much needed caffeine fix. Everyone was in a rush. Everyone, except this girl. I remember noticing her, first, because she seemed to be the only person in the whole cafe who was still. It almost looked as though she had been frozen in time, gazing intently at her book, without even moving her stare as she drank from her teacup. Then I noticed the book: the words *Systems of Psychotherapy* blazing from the page. I was so used to seeing people reading the latest Katie Price autobiography, or *Fifty Shades of Grey*, that those words, that cover, stood out. And then it occurred to me; there I was, on my way home from my job at Lush, arms covered in glitter, having just finished a degree I didn't even enjoy, with no real clue about the rest of my life; what was I missing? There she was, looking like she had it all sorted. I found myself imagining how she must have this great flat, with a great boyfriend, with this interesting job that meant she read books like *Systems of Psychotherapy*. She even wore glasses! Can you get any classier and intelligent than that?

"LARGE CARAMEL LATTE WITH CREAM TO GO."

1

And the spell was broken.

*

I've never been able to read with too much background noise, which probably makes the Costa in the middle of town at lunchtime an unwise choice. But, quite frankly, I've been living the same routine every day for months and I need a change. I'll try being one of those smart, sophisticated women who reads books in coffee shops and meets the man of their dreams when he comes over and asks what her book is about...anyway. Mind wandering. Bloody hell that coffee machine is loud! Right. The development of cognitive therapy hit me.

Damn, there's a smudge on my glasses. Maybe I can read around it.

Nope. This is hopeless, it's right in the middle.

Okay, let's assess the room.

Why is that girl staring at me? Crap, maybe I'm pink, it is warm in here. It's so busy too, and I can't clean that smudge while she's staring at me! She hasn't even looked away now I've looked at her. Oh, God, it must be bad!

Oh, thank goodness for that, she's got her caramel latte. The coast is clear. Right, where's my tissue...

*

Right, I'm gonna cut in here. First by being analytical me and pointing out how *incredible* it is that two people can experience the same, distant interaction, in *completely* different ways. People's minds are so interesting!

Now that's out of the way, I put it to you; which of those girls is more insecure? Trick question; they're both as bad as each other, obviously. Sure, the Lush girl is an imaginary person, based on how I imagine one individual might have perceived me on that day. But the reader? The reader is me. Aged twenty-three, having just started a master's degree in psychotherapy (the dream, by the way), feeling totally overwhelmed by juggling working in a shop, studying, going for therapy, supervision, trying to get a placement, feeling desperately lonely (single as hell), and trying to support the people I love. Pretty self-explanatory, day-to-day stresses, right?

But that doesn't explain why cleaning my glasses has become a dramatic internal monologue, whereby the entire room must be observed and examined for any threats. I mean, what's the big deal? You just take them off, do that hot, quick breath to steam the lenses up, give them a quick whizz with whatever fabric you can find, jobs a good 'un. Right?

Wrong.

Not in my world. Not in my own, uniquely experienced, individually shaped, and totally subjective world.

I realise I'm setting this up to be some epic, dramatic tale. Trust me, it's no *Titanic*. It's just some ramblings of a girl who often feels misunderstood, judged, and labelled by friends and colleagues. And complete strangers. Purely because of one tiny aspect of the way she looks. So hey, I'll make my case, explain, describe, and bare my soul. And you can decide for yourself why that twenty-three-year-old girl is so afraid of cleaning her glasses in a cafe.

*

Part 1: Childhood

I'd like to introduce you to me, age four. Age four with short brown hair and scabby knees from falling over on the same bit of pavement every day. Age four with no idea what the words *loneliness, prejudice, discrimination,* or *bullying* mean. A confident, young girl with a gung-ho approach to everything she does. These are some of my most vivid early memories, all framed by that one, particular thing that makes cleaning my glasses scary.

*

If there is one photo that captures my true spirit, it's this one. Behold, the sheer joy of a child making snowballs and living life without a care in the world. This little girl is still very much present in my life, especially when it snows!

*

"Why do you have that patch on your eye?"
"Mummy said it's to make my eyes better because I

keep falling over."

"Oh, okay. Want to go and play in the sand pit?"

"Yeah, okay!"

*

This chair is massive, my feet don't even touch the floor! This room is a funny shape, it's so small and bright. I don't like the lights, they're so bright. I wonder why there are so many thank you cards on the walls? Maybe they're for the man who will make my eyes better. I hope I don't have to do all those looking things again, the light he shone in my eyes was too bright. Oh, Mummy looks serious. I wonder why?

*

This thing on the back of my hand feels really weird, I don't like it. It's making my hand feel all tingly. This woman wants me to play, but it's really hard to play with this sticker on my hand. Mummy and Daddy have their serious faces is on, so maybe if I do what this lady says they won't be as serious.

*

"Chloe, you can't keep shutting your eyes every time the drop gets close to your eye!"

"But I don't like it!"

*

It's hard to describe fully how it felt to be the only girl in nursery wearing glasses or the only girl at primary school who had to wear a patch on her eye. Mostly because all I have is snippets. Key moments where people were asking me questions that weren't, "Do you need the toilet?" or "What colour pen would you like to use?" like they asked the other kids. Instead, they were asking me questions like, "Are you in pain?" or "Why do your eyes look like that?" or "Tell me which letters you can read." It was only when I started doing things outside my usual bubble of safety that I began to feel like my differences weren't something to be celebrated. That's when the battle started. The battle between childhood innocence and acceptance, and the reality of prejudice and judgement. Who among us have been told by their parents that it's okay to be different because that's what makes you who you are! Try believing that when everyone *but* your parents is telling you something different.

*

This moment encapsulates my fears, my vulnerability and most importantly, my courage. What you can't see is my heart beating ten to the dozen, but what you can see is me feeling the fear and doing it anyway.

"Gymnastics. I'd really like to try gymnastics."
Gymnastics.

We've all watched the Olympics on TV. We've seen
the strong, muscled, agile athletes throwing themselves
at a vault, swinging around on a bar, pulling off gravity
defying routines on springy floors. I wanted to be like
them. And so in my determined, gung-ho way, I joined a
local gymnastics group and found my calling. I'm now a
world famous gymnast with hundreds of gold medals.

Just kidding. I was pretty good actually. But
gymnastics was a defining moment in my life for more
than one reason. Those death-defying stunts meant that if
I wore my glasses, we'd be replacing them on a weekly
basis. This meant I'd do the full session visually impaired,
if you like. I couldn't judge distances. You can imagine
how that ended when I was hurtling myself towards a
spring board and vault at high speed with no room for error
(let's just say I think my mum was glad when I quit).

But that never bothered me.

What bothered me was what the other children's eyes
were doing. There I would be, standing in line waiting
for my turn on the bar, chalk on my hands, blisters on
my palms from the friction. On the other side of the mats
would be another line of children waiting for their turn
on the beam. In the corner, a line of girls waiting to run
at the vault. And in each of these lines, there would be
at least one person looking. Staring directly at my eyes.
Staring, unblinking, uncaring, obvious, staring. Whispers
to one another without breaking the gaze in my direction.
I remember thinking *haven't their parents ever told them
staring is rude?* I never asked myself the question, "Why
are they staring at me?" I knew why. It was obvious why.
But that didn't stop me feeling like I had this big red target
on my forehead, singling me out for attack. I have never
felt more alone, more isolated, or more different than I did

in those gymnastics lessons.

But that was nothing compared to what happened a few years later.

*

"Now you've got a choice, Chloe. You can either come on the rowing boat with me and your brother, or you and Dad can do something different."

"Swimming!"

You know how people talk about fateful decisions that set them on a fateful course of events that changed their lives for ever and so on? This was sort of like that. I think we probably all have certain moments in our lives that we can look back on and feel all the same feelings we did then, as if we were right back there and it had only just happened.

Picture it. A father and daughter at a big holiday swimming park, having some quality time. Laughing, splashing each other, enjoying themselves. The girl can only be about twelve or thirteen. Then you notice that there's something unusual about the girl's eyes. What would you do? Think, *Oh, that's different,* and then get on with having your own fun? I like to think most people would do that. And normally, adults would.

By this point, I expected staring and questions or comments from other children. Even at the tender age of twelve, I knew that it was just because they didn't understand rather than them trying to inflict pain.

Adults were safe. I trusted adults to be kind. Or not say anything at all. After all, my parents were adults and they were the kindest people in the world. All I was doing that day was having some real, love-filled fun with my dad, my hero. And then I looked over and saw this group of four adults. Two men, two women; all staring at me. All four of them. One of the men's faces changed into what can only be described as a grimace. Then I heard six words I'll never forget.

"Ugh, what's wrong with her eyes?"

Match that with the look of disgust and you've got the most earth shattering moment of my whole life up until that point. The only phrase that does the feeling any justice is this: soul destroying.

Just process that in your mind for a second.

Just imagine being on the receiving end of that.

Grown-ups actively and openly judging and criticising an innocent child.

Every fear you've always had about being different and unacceptable being realised.

Childhood innocence, erased.

The belief that the world is all good and that your parents can keep you safe from anything and anyone, erased.

*

Part 2: Adolescence

Adolescence. One of the most confusing, conflicting and discombobulating times of anyone's life. Imagine it: a comprehensive secondary school of around fourteen hundred students. Each year group containing hundreds of sweaty, loud and opinionated teenagers from a colourful spectrum of backgrounds. Put an already self-conscious, spectacled, well-spoken, conscientious girl with a visual dissimilarity in the middle of it all, and you've got a recipe for disaster. At times it was almost like when you see a loose helium balloon being buffeted by high winds. Hit into buildings and trees, blowing one way the next, then being violently redirected by a sudden gust.

*

The second most prominent phrase in my life after the swimming pool incident, is probably this:

"Are you looking at me or him?"

Allow me to explain. Many, many children have something called a squint, whereby the muscles controlling their eyes don't quite work and one eye will wander; it'll either turn inwards (towards your nose) or outwards (towards your ear). Normally, a patch on the eye for a while fixes it. An eye patch and two operations by the age of four later, and the eye doctors decided I was...wait for it…"rare."

Essentially, the part of my brain that controls combining the image from one eye with the image from the other eye is defective. This means that in an attempt to have one, single image in my brain, one eye will attempt to look at the same point in space as the other. Thus causing the eye to turn inwards. Make sense? No? Jolly good. Took a shed load of diagrams for it to make any sense to me too.

But essentially I have what many people would term a lazy eye or if you want the more abrupt version, bozz-eyed.

Which has countless number of times caused my peers to say:

"Are you looking at me or him?"

Ever tried playing Wink Murder in drama when people can't tell whether you're making eye contact with them or the person next to them? Every bloody week (pardon my French) we played that game in drama and it was torture.

*

Now, I'll be honest. My time at secondary school was

probably the same level of difficult as it was for most. Not the best, not the worst. No fortune on earth could be paid to me to make me go back, mind you. So, in many ways, I see no use in delving into the particulars of this time. All you need to know is that it was hard for me to make eye contact with anyone at all for fear of being noticed. Caught out. *Discovered.*

Years of suppressing that gung-ho, fearless girl led me to a relatively monumental decision: operation number three. Age sixteen. My choice, my right. My time to take control of something I wished desperately that I didn't have. My attempt to be more normal. Key point: the word "more" in that sentence. I always knew I couldn't be cured completely because I was "rare," but I could at least soften the blow of being different a bit. And so, I did it.

So there I was, 7.30 a.m. at the QMC with my wonderful, strong, supportive parents by my side. There it was, that all too familiar hospital smell, but this time they didn't give me the hand numbing cream. As much as I hated it as a four-year-old, boy, did I wish they'd blooming well given it to me as a sixteen-year-old! It doesn't half hurt when they stick a needle in the back of your hand! I'll never forget being wheeled into the anaesthetic room and feeling like I'd entered the set of a *Monty Python* sketch. These two blokes in scrubs were a double act John Cleese and Eric Idle would have been proud of. Their tongue-in-cheek wittering about how quickly I would "go under" was strangely reassuring.

I won't bore you with the details of recovery, only so far as to say it was long, painful, and extremely inconvenient. You try being a gung-ho, fearless sort of person when you can't even open your eyes or wash your own hair!

Suffice to say, I got the desired outcome. I went from being able to see my wonky eyes in every picture that was taken of me, to looking in the mirror and, when wearing glasses, seeing two straight eyes. Bliss.

*

Bliss, until... driving.

As it turned out, the operation did two things. It straightened my eyes by a few degrees and in the process gave me double vision. Double vision soon became the new bane of my life. My older brother was learning to drive, along with three of my close friends and large quantities of the population of sixth form. As it transpired at one of my follow up appointments, I would be deemed "legally unsafe" on the road due to my visual impairment. You know how we talked about those earth shattering moments in life that we all experience to varying degrees? There was another one. Another choice gone.

I'd find myself sitting at the dinner table listening to my family talk about the complexities of a three-point turn, stopping distances and brake pedals. I'd zone out because it was easier than dealing with the reality of being somehow separate to my family.

*

Part 3: Adulthood

Really, I'm only at the start of this chapter of my life, so I'll keep it brief.

I'm hoping those snapshots of my life have explained why cleaning my glasses takes a monumental amount of courage. You've had a rollercoaster tour of my misery memoire and key sufferings in life. So what next? Did this vivacious, gung-ho girl live the next five years as a recluse, afraid of grabbing life by the horns? It probably wouldn't come as a surprise if that had been what happened.

But it wasn't what happened.

What was my saving grace, I hear you ask? Drama. That's right. Acting, performing, arty-farty expression. Standing up on stage in front of people and singing, improvising, reciting lines, burning under the lights. You might call it exposure therapy and in many ways, that's exactly what it was. It forced me to confront my fear; being stared at. But it was staring that was my choice, under my control. And they weren't staring at me because I was different. They were staring at me because that's exactly what you do when you're watching someone perform. It offered me a strange sort of anonymity and protection. I wasn't me on that stage, I was Elphaba from *Wicked*, or Eponine from *Les Miserables*. And I did it well. Boy, did I do it well.

Doing it well has led me to achieve things that twelve-year-old girl would never have believed would happen.

I achieved a degree in Creative Expressive Therapies, specialising in Drama. I worked with children with learning disabilities and adults with life-limiting illnesses to improve their self-esteem, communication, confidence, and self-expression. I used drama to help them fulfil their potential despite their barriers, the same way drama helped me. It's got rather a nice continuity to it, don't you think?

I travelled across the world to Canada, the biggest trip of my life, and swam with strangers in lakes. I swam. With strangers. In lakes. Yes, at times I had that holiday swimming pool memory invading its way into my mind, but instead of trying to ignore it, I welcomed it. The fear came with me.

And finally, the biggest achievement yet. I am now a practicing trainee counsellor/psychotherapist working with young and bereaved people.

Why is that the biggest achievement, you might ask?

It's my dream. It's who I am.

When I was four, Gramps died (I promise this is relevant). My nana moved up to live closer to us not long after. A few years ago I was at her house cutting a particularly unruly shrub for her, and somewhere in that day I found myself asking her about her grief. She got a box out, filled with birthday cards, drawings, and notes. A box of love. And she'd kept a note I'd written. Age four. It said something like:

"We all miss Gramps too. I know you're sad. I love you lots."

At age four, the bits of my brain that held my compassion, empathy, and love were there in full force. I've often wondered whether I would have written that note, if I would be as loving as I am if I didn't have wonky eyes.

At the core of me, I want to help other people to cope with their struggles, their pain, their hurt, their isolation. I have struggled, I have felt pain, I have been hurt, I have felt isolated. And I have come out the other end strong, compassionate, open-minded, non-judgemental, open-hearted...I could go on. I'm not perfect, no one is. But those comments and stares haven't scarred me, they've shaped me.

One of my favourite quotes comes from Susan Jeffers, and it encompasses my attitude to life and my biggest lesson from being different.

"Feel the fear and do it anyway."

Courage, perseverance, stubbornness, determination, and strength of spirit. These are the words behind this moment. In times of insecurity, I look at this photo and say to myself, "But look at what you've achieved. Don't be such a scaredy-cat. You can and you will."

Party Night
Margaret White

8th May, 1941, Nottingham

I was seventeen and always looked forward to the weekly social session at the church hall. Having left school at fourteen and working now with older people, it was a chance to catch up with people my own age and relax after a hard day at work. We usually played badminton, but tonight I was more excited than usual because we were going to have a party.

I had taken a bit longer to get ready and I had chosen to wear my favourite dress. It was purple crepe; my mum had made it, as she was a very clever seamstress, which was lucky as it was difficult to buy clothes. You had to use clothing coupons, but these were needed to buy clothes for work. I never found out where Mum had got the material from. I loved the dress; it was narrow at the waist but full at the hem. Because of the material it seemed to float out when I turned around. I was also wearing the much maligned rayon stockings. These were very thick, not at all like nylon stockings, but those were impossible to buy during the war.

So I walked the short distance from my house to the hall. You couldn't miss it, it looked like a huge garden shed, both inside and out. But it housed a badminton court, kitchen, and toilets.

It had turned out to be a really nice evening. We were all

chattering and dancing and felt relaxed. Then we suddenly went silent.

The dreaded air raid siren had started up. We froze on the spot and listened; we couldn't hear any planes but soon rushed home anyway. We had never been bombed and there'd been many sirens sounded over the last few months which hadn't amounted to anything, so although we followed procedure, we weren't frightened.

When I got home me and Mum sat up chatting in the kitchen. There had been no aircraft noise so we hadn't scurried down to the cellar steps, which was the area of the house we used as an air raid shelter, but we hadn't risked going to bed, either. After what seemed like hours with no noise, but no all clear siren, we finally risked going to bed.

I must have nodded off and gone into a light sleep, but suddenly I was bolt upright in bed. I could hear a plane and it sounded very close. My heart was thumping so hard I thought it might burst.

"Margaret, move. Quick, get to the cellar steps!"

I didn't need telling twice. I leapt out of bed and raced downstairs in only my nightie.

We had only just made it when we heard whizzing noises. These were incendiary or fire bombs being dropped. The whizzing noises came in pulses as waves of aeroplanes passed over. In between the pulses of the firebomb planes were the deeper sounds of the big bomber planes. I don't know how long we sat on those cold, hard, concrete steps, but it seemed like a lifetime. But we were oblivious to the cold and damp as fear had taken over. We just sat there, gripping each other in a tight hug. We really thought our lives could end at any moment; at best, we thought the house would be damaged. The planes were so loud it seemed like they were almost touching the roof.

Eventually, the skies fell quiet, but it was some time before the all clear was sounded. By the time we made it back up to the kitchen it was too late to go back to bed, as it was nearly time to get up and get ready for work. So we had a cup of tea and I got ready to go to work.

I always walked quite fast to work. It was a long way, but there was never any public transport. I was only a street away when I met Mary; she was quite a bit older than me and worked in a different department. We both worked at Boots Printing Works on Station Street, close to the railway station. It was a huge factory.

"Hello, are you going to look at the bombing damage?" asked Mary as she waited for me to catch her up.

We carried on walking, and I felt a bit confused. "What bombing damage?" I asked.

Before Mary could reply we turned the corner. The Printing Works was a pile of rubble, dust, and what seemed to be confetti was blowing in the wind. But it wasn't conventional confetti, this was printed with Boots the Chemist on each flake. Only one small block of the factory was still standing.

We had a bombing raid the following night as well. Four hundred and twenty-four bombs were dropped over the course of the two nights. One hundred and fifty-nine people died; forty-nine worked at the Co-Op bakery on the night shift, which was close to our factory. Two hundred and seventy-four people were injured, again a lot from the bakery, who had suffered severe burns. The local air raid warden at Boots was a young man around my age; he was one of the ones to lose his life.

We were lucky to have escaped unharmed and I'm forever grateful for not having to work night shifts, or I might not have been here to tell my story. All the printing firms in Nottingham got together and gave jobs to those who needed work. I got to stay working in the little bit of the factory that didn't get destroyed. Eventually, they rebuilt it. I think it was even better than the original.

From West Country to Up Country
Brian T. Munson

1st April, 1958

I was boarding the troopship Empire Fowey en route to the Aden Peninsula, along with several hundred other servicemen. I was just eighteen years old and had spent the last year doing basic training and trade training as an airframe mechanic in the Royal Air Force. At that time in the country there was conscription, and I was due to be conscripted because of my age and because I was not in a reserve occupation (like farming). In 1958 the country was still recovering from the war, and there were still plenty of conflicts happening all over the world, meaning they still needed plenty of soldiers. I was going to go in anyway, as there was no real industry or work where I was living.

We were being directed to F deck. For those who have never been on or seen a troopship, F deck is for the lower ranks and is generally below the waterline, the part of the ship which gets flooded first should anything untoward happen.

The sleeping arrangements consisted of three double rows of bunks, three high, with the person on the top bunk sleeping with his nose almost touching the deck above. I was on the top bunk, and to get into my bunk, because there was a large ventilation duct running close to my hips,

I had to get onto the bed from the other bed, and I couldn't turn over in the night because my hips were too wide. But you just accept these things, don't you? As far as I was concerned, it was all exciting and fantastic. While a lot of others may have resented it, I wasn't one of them.

The ship left Southampton at 1600 hours and headed down the channel into the Bay of Biscay, turning south to Gibraltar where some of the troops were to be disembarked. The bay lived up to its reputation and those with weaker stomachs were bringing up their breakfasts, which by any standards really wasn't worth keeping down. I could keep the plastic eggs down with no problem, although you could use the bacon as a window because it was so thin.

Having been brought up on Exmoor in Somerset, I was extremely naive to the ways of the world and the trip was fast becoming a very steep learning curve. The first lesson was not to stand down wind of someone leaning over side in a storm.

It took three days to reach Gibraltar due to the bad weather, which meant only men destined there left the ship, and four hours later we were on our way. Next stop: Malta.

The sea was calm, blue and inviting, but as the Captain was trying to make up lost time, the stop was the same as Gibraltar, quick and official. Next stop: Cyprus.

The Suez crisis had meant that all non-Egyptian vessels had to sail through the Suez Canal in convoy and with armed Egyptian soldiers on board, so there were several days of relaxation while we waited to join the other ships. You weren't allowed to sunbathe, because if you got sunburnt it was considered a self-inflicted injury and you were penalized with extra duties (often cleaning up the mess from the drinking the night before). So I stayed out of the sun, but I played cards for cigarettes (even though I didn't smoke, so it didn't matter what I bet).

During the conflict President Nasser had ordered the sinking of several ships to blockade the canal. In 1958 a passage had been cleared as the sovereignty of the canal had been secured from the French and the British.

The Red Sea was magical, crystal clear water with desert sands on either side and dolphins riding the ship's bow wave. Imagine the impression it had on a young lad from the West Country.

My elder brother, who was in the Royal Navy, told me that you could smell Aden before you could see it, but that was a bit of an exaggeration.

Steamer point was where the ship docked and all the remaining troops disembarked into various sections to await transport to their destinations. It was so unusual to go into that environment that you just had to absorb everything going on around you. With the friends I made on board, we were on our way to Khormaksar, the RAF base there. The spices and the food they were eating were so different from home. It was great.

Our first night was spent under canvas at the transit camp, as an introduction to life in hot and humid Aden.

The next morning after breakfast, which was cooked on a field kitchen, we were assembled in ranks of three and marched through the station living quarters where all the old hands, "the done-a-bits," were leaning over the rails shouting derisive remarks at the new comers. In a few months, it would be our turn.

The reception desk allocated billets, beds, and anything else admin could conjure up. I was sent to block two, middle floor, with the instructions to find a bed among the twenty-two others not occupied.

I arrived at 78 Squadron at 0700 hours and reported to the squadron office. Next to the office was the crew room where I introduced myself to my fellow engineers. I was given the flight manuals on the Single Pioneer aircraft to read and inwardly digest.

The aircraft wasn't at all complicated, but the safety of the crew and any passengers was paramount, so being keen to advance I took any tasks very seriously.

The next couple of months were spent acclimatising and walking around Steamer Point looking at the shops and the market. Being a duty free port there were bargains to be had, especially where cameras were concerned. I got one, and I made good use of it (when I began writing this story it was because I was looking through some of those old photographs). You had to send the film off to be developed in the UK, and at the time the most popular photos were on 35mm colour slides, of which I have several hundred.

I learned that there were several airstrips up country carved out of rocks and stones where a Single Pioneer could land, namely Dhala, which was close to the Yemeni border, and Beit el Falage, in Trucial Oman, close to the town of Muscat.

It was to Beit el Falage that, contrary to all advice, I volunteered to go with the XL701 on detachment. The flight was to take us along the coast from Khormaksar with an overnight refueling stop at Masirah island, and then on to Muscat.

After refueling and leaving essential supplies to the medics, we left at daybreak to avoid the scorching sun for most of the seven-hour flight across the empty quarter.

To relieve the boredom on such a long, slow flight the pilot let myself and Pat Murphy take turns at the controls by shuffling around the cockpit and then sitting in the pilot seat. Quite exciting at five thousand feet above the desert!

The facilities when we arrived in Beit el Falage were quite rudimentary, as it was still being established as a permanent base; a field kitchen and camp beds with mosquito nets under canvas. The shower was open air, of course, consisting of an ex-avgas forty gallon fuel drum on a wooden structure equipped with a shower rose and a tap. The drum was filled every morning from the well to get warm during the day. Did I say warm?

Two or three days later, late in the afternoon, the CO received a call that a casualty needed to be evacuated from a small village called Awabi, an hour or so flying time down the coast, and then half an hour inland.

We got the XL701 ready and put on board a box of illumination flares as night descends quickly in the desert. I wasn't nervous, it was just good to get on with it. We'd been waiting around for quite a while for the doctor to show up.

It was practice on our squadron that airframe mechanics be trained on engine problems and vice versa, with the idea that a mechanic should fly with each mission. Len and I used to take it in turns and, yes! It was my turn to be the mechanic on duty.

We were told that the casualty was a member of the Trucial Omen Scouts, an army loyal to the Sultan of Oman being supported and trained by the British. He had driven his Landrover over a land mine and lost part of his leg. This needed the services of a local doctor as the wound was beyond the training of the patrol medic.

It was dark when the pilot turned inland and started to search for Awabi and some indication from the patrol on the ground. It was common practice in that area to light up the landing strip by using the headlights of two Landrovers, one either side of the threshold pointing down the strip. We also used cut in half beer cans full of sand, put petrol in them, and then set them on fire and set them along each side of the runway. They would act like flares.

After circling the date palms and trying to decipher the signals from the ground, the pilot asked me to fire a flare to light up the area. He then decided to land.

We watched the lights of the vehicles along the tracks leading to the landing ground as we made our approach. Coming low over the palms he throttled back to drop down at the start of the strip, only to find a vehicle parked in the way. The landing gear was ripped off as the aircraft crashed onto the vehicle and continued into the other Land Rover at the far end of strip, which had its headlights on full beam, blinding the pilot. I had jettisoned the doors in case we had a fire; thankfully not. It was of course nerve wracking; to lose your landing gear and belly flop onto the runway wasn't a simple thing.

I helped the doctor out of the wreckage to give more room for the pilot to get out, who then confronted the officer commanding the Army patrol. I overheard a few expletives while I busied myself turning off fuel cocks, electrical isolators, and generally checking around the plane. Astoundingly, none of us were hurt.

The doctor had been taken to the casualty (who wasn't as badly injured as it had first appeared), and nothing more could be done except place guards around the site and then turn in for the remainder of the night. We were driven to where the army had set up a secure camp. The Flight Lieutenant pilot was given a camp bed with other officers, while I found myself a place to bed down in the other tent and fell asleep immediately.

Next morning, after eggs and beans, we were driven to the plane where I started to remove the valuable and attractive items such as the radio, batteries, and other things that could be useful to the local tribesmen. Some fuel was drained from the wing tanks into jerry cans, and then the wreckage was set on fire. That way it was destroyed so no one else could even use the metal.

Three days later we were back at Beit el Falage, after sitting on top of a lightly armed, six-wheeled vehicle called a Ferret (not the most comfortable of journeys). The patient we'd gone to see had his right leg dressed and a shot of morphine and was made comfortable on a stretcher in one of the remaining Land Rovers. He'd be taken back to Bait el Falage and then on to Muscat.

We stopped every evening (no street lights or cafes in the desert) to eat and rest. The Arab soldiers did the cooking, which was generally a stew-like dish mainly of red lentils and vegetables in a large pot where everyone helped themselves by tearing off lumps from a chapatti and scooping up the stew using the chapatti as a spoon. It was all so interesting and new, and we'd sit around and talk in the evenings. There was no light pollution and I spent plenty of time looking at the stars, even though it could drop very cold at night.

On arrival Beit el Falage, I was told to pack my kit as I was going back to Khormaksar for a medical checkup and the inquiry about the plane crash. We left early the next morning in a twin-engine Pembroke en route to Sharjah, where we were to transfer to a Valletta of Transport Command.

I was rather disappointed that my time was being cut short at Beit el Falage as the very simple living was beginning to grow on me; it was bringing out the native in me. It was so simple and such an easy life. It was hot, and I didn't mind the rudimentary facilities. I'd grown to quite like the solitude.

The inquiry was, as all military procedures were, a very formal affair; best uniform, highly polished shoes, bright shiny cap badge, and pressed shirt and trousers. Trying to find a shirt without oil stains was quite a task.

My involvement at the inquiry was quite small as I reiterated the events of the night to the Station Commander, his Adjutant, 78 Squadron CO, and his Adjutant. Notes were taken, questions asked, and eventually I was dismissed and told my evidence would be typed for my perusal and signature. This was daunting, standing in front of a wing commander; more than the plane crash, really.

I was soon back on duty at the squadron, drinking mugs of extremely strong tea which we bought from an Arab boy who made it in a Burko boiler. The brew got stronger as the day progressed as "Chico", as he was affectionately known, tipped more Brooke Bond leaves into the boiling water. I'm sure he obtained his supplies from the back of the cookhouse. The tea was diluted with copious amounts of Carnation evaporated milk, but it kept us going. I can't remember who said it, but someone did: "The English and their bloody tea."

More border incidents were reported, and I couldn't wait for my next trip "up country."

The Kitten
Betty Scott

A Childhood Memory

When I was younger I used to like writing stories. This one I showed to my sister and she said that it was really good. This was saying something as I didn't really get on with my sister very well. I think I was about fifteen. I was good at English and I enjoyed reading. I started off with Enid Blyton and graduated to Agatha Christie and Catherine Cookson. I liked a good mystery, but it didn't have to have a happy ending.

This story is partly true and partly fiction. I remember having a tabby cat called Tish and she had kittens. But we only needed one cat in the house to catch the mice and I think my dad was worried about keeping all of the kittens so they were drowned. This story has a happier ending and is made up of memories as a child when all the days seemed sunny and full of happy things like picnics and paddling in the river at the bottom of Woodborough Road.

My Story

A little boy was being looked after by his big brother. His mum had gone to the shops and she had told his older brother to look after him. His older brother was a bit of a bully, not a nasty one, but it did mean that he had to do as he was told. His older brother didn't really want to look after him. He'd rather be out playing with his mates, but he had no choice and had to do as he was told.

They ran down the steep hill to the banks of the stream. They weren't allowed to play in the river as they weren't big enough. It was a lovely sunny summer's day, and they took a picnic with them. In those days a picnic was made up of bread and jam and a bottle of water. On the way down they saw the horses in the fields.

At the side of the stream there were banks to get down to the water where they paddled. While they were paddling they saw a kitten. It looked like someone had thrown it in the water. The older brother managed to pull the kitten out. It was a pretty tabby cat so he took off his jumper, wrapped the kitten up, and took it home to their mother.

But Mother said they couldn't keep the kitten and sent them back to the stream. This upset them both very much. When they were by the banks of the stream with the little kitten, a stranger came along and asked them if they knew what they were going to do with the kitten. She said that she wanted a kitten and took him home. The boys were pleased to see him go home with someone, rather than leaving him by the river to fend for himself.

The Greatest Prize of All
Tessa Marie

Quiet and alone
No one to talk to,
Sitting here sad,
So quiet
I wish I had someone to talk to,
But no one feels like talking to me

That's how you feel when you have a family but feel
totally alone. I was a young mum, thinking I was the
worst mother in the world because I had this child who just
wanted to hide from the world, and I didn't know what to
do with him. People asked, "Why is your child like that?" or
said "He needs to learn to play," and then there was the man
on a till in Sainsbury's who said, "That child will do nothing
in life if he stays that shy."

People can be so cruel with their passing comments,
and I remember each and every one. I see their faces,
the location, and I relive that sinking feeling with each
memory. I had no support, you see. I had a husband who
was always down the pub or out with his mates (this was
not the only problem but I only realised that later). I was
always on my own, trying to integrate this little boy into
life (Kindermusik classes, mother and toddler, day care),
but each activity was met with heart breaking screams or a

little boy who wouldn't move off my lap. The frustration I felt was immense. At times I felt like I was falling apart, like the walls were crushing in on me and my poor little boy was caught in the middle.

It was only after having my outgoing daughter that I knew something was wrong, but my cries for help to my husband were ignored. I felt frustrated, like I was going mad, and I tried to get him to help me, but I was pushed aside, made to feel like I'd failed, almost laughed at. He wouldn't listen to me or even communicate with me; he had his life and I was the person who was there to look after the children and home. He just wanted to be out at the pub. He controlled me you see, just by the way he set the day up. I was never given any hugs or kind words of support; I was a service tool at his disposal, but having never had it any other way, I just thought it was my lot, even although I knew it was wrong and my confidence was at rock bottom. I felt at the very end of my tether; any woman will know where I am coming from. I was being swallowed down a never ending spiral and found anger beyond all comprehension and I did not like the person I was becoming. I was surrounded by a toxic energy, I guess you could've called it depression. You see my husband fueled this, fanning the flames, egging me on, getting this sick satisfaction with what he could do with me.

At school one day, the teaching assistant took me to one side outside of the school gates and asked me, "Don't you ever cuddle your son? It will really make a difference, you know?" Yes, she really said that to me. I took my beautiful little boy and his little sister, and they never went back to that school again.

It was then that I pushed, oh, I really pushed, for medical support for my son and some understanding. The answer came a few years later; my not so little boy was diagnosed with Asperger's syndrome. The sense of relief

was overwhelming. I read the books and I understood…
well, I tried to, but by then it was ingrained in me that I was
on my own, that my husband would rather be anywhere
else than at home. He gave me no emotional support, he
emotionally controlled me, and I was sad to the bone.

So this was where I was, sitting in my bedroom in the
dark, praying to God to get me out of this mess, because I
just couldn't do it on my own.

And do you know what? I was given that strength that
night, and it came from a really unexpected source. It was
two of my volunteers at work in one of my charity shops
that I ran, and they just *knew* I needed support. I had always
been a closed book, rushing from meeting to meeting from
shop to shop, always the smiling one, always the doer, never
the slacker. But suddenly there I was in my little book shop
with a volunteer that was looking at me—I mean, really
looking. I felt his eyes boring into my soul.

"You're troubled," he said. "Tell me. You must tell
me."

It seems so odd now, looking back, but it felt like it
was the first time I had ever been looked at. It was in that
moment, that flash of a moment, that I knew, with no doubt
in my mind that this was how a woman *should* be looked at,
and I had never, ever, had that experience. How can you go
through fourteen years of marriage and not know that? And
then a day later in my furniture shop another volunteer said,
"You must tell me. Please tell me. I can help you."

She was so kind. She made me feel safe, made me
believe that I could, and would, cope with what was about
to come. So there it was; my pivotal moment, the turning
point in my life. It took all my courage and nerve, but I did
it. I left on a road to find me, to feel safe, and to love myself.
The road was rough, but my son grew into a wonderful man.
I made it and I found me; the greatest prize of all.

A Memory Walk
Kerry Lovell

Alzheimer's Disease is an ever growing concern, and many of us know a friend or family member with this condition. My father was diagnosed when he was eighty, and he died seven years later. It was a long and difficult time for all the family, none more so than for my mum, who looked after him at home. So, when Mum was diagnosed with dementia at the same age of eighty, we had some idea of what to expect.

That's why I've signed up the last two years for a Memory Walk arranged by the Alzheimer's Society. They aren't a huge physical challenge; just a five or ten kilometre walk around Wollaton Park in Nottingham. As a family we often visited Wollaton Hall and Museum to see the giraffe and the lovely gardens with the grand greenhouses and orangery. We came at all times of the year; picnics in the summer with the deer gently grazing in the centre field, where we used to roll down the big hill in front of the Hall, and we'd go sledging there in the winter. I took my own children to do the same.

As a child, I remember seeing my mum run into the centre of a herd of deer. A stag had been disturbed by children playing too close and, wanting to protect the herd, was preparing to toss a little girl up in the air. Mum saw what was happening, ran into the field, and scooped the little girl up before any harm could come to her. That was a striking moment that happened so quickly, but I'll never forget it.

I also remember walking around the lake with my father on a fundraising event organised in his role as vice-chair of the Sports and Social Club at Plessey in Beeston. It was just Dad and me, and I don't recall raising a lot of money, but I do remember the walk, and Dad's calm and gentle stride alongside mine.

In the days after Dad's funeral we went there as a family to walk around the grounds. It was Christmas time and I have the photographs of my children, now grown up, but still enjoying the park in the winter sunshine. It was a strange combination of Christmas celebrations and adjusting to the loss of Dad, focusing on trying to remember him as he was before the disease took him. We had lost my dad years before he died. It seemed fitting to make a visit to Wollaton beyond this event and a welcome coincidence that the Alzheimer's society event should be held there.

The Memory Walk was set in September. Surely the weather would be all right, but the rain clouds were gathering as I arrived. Not sure what to expect, I parked on a nearby street and came through the side entrance, past the deer field on the left, and I was enjoying the hint of autumnal colours. But as I came around the corner I saw a blanket of blue T-shirts and coats. So many people. There was a loud and lively stage, and we were encouraged to warm up with Zumba and be jollied along by the music. I looked around to see many people, generations of families, dogs with little T-shirts and neckerchiefs. As I had come alone I was instantly reassured by their presence, but it also allowed me a time of reflection. It was a revelation to see the numbers on a page of research or in the news when talking about the rise in this condition represented by real people.

There was a Memory Tree to write a message, and that was a poignant moment, seeing it in black and white, but there was positive theme of people wanting to raise money for a future without dementia. It was hard to hang my message on the tree for Mum and Dad, a message on behalf of myself, my brother, and my children. Difficult to realise this was for both of them, representing the past, present, and future.

Soon the horn sounded and off we set, snaking up the hill, when the heavens opened and didn't stop. There were many of those large plastic capes with a hood and arms, but even that didn't hold the rain back. The ground underfoot was soggy, but the dogs didn't appear to mind. It was a remarkable sight, and I felt glad to be part of this memory. I've seen plenty of sports events and marathons on the TV, but it was still a small triumph to see the finish line with happy faces handing out medals and cheering us on.

As I turned to go home I looked back at the many people supporting this cause; it's good to know you aren't alone. I went over to Mum's and picked up where I had left off, listening to her childhood stories of the war and helping her to muddle through the rest of the day.

When my dad died, ten years ago now, I was still working as a teacher but knew that I wanted a change of career. I have a strong faith and felt a clear direction had been placed in front of me. I'd had a taste of working through a range of processes and systems to get the help needed for Mum and Dad. I wanted to be involved in some way, maybe to give something back. I was certainly aware of an ever growing need for resources and at the same time fascinated by the complexities of health and social care. I can remember the look on my children's and family faces when I said I had applied through UCAS to study for three years full time at Sheffield Hallam University to gain a degree in Occupational Therapy. My eldest daughter was already at university, my son was applying, and my youngest daughter was in upper school. As it turned out we took it in turns to study for exams, to complete assignments, and to graduate.

My training and subsequent working life has been rewarding beyond words. It is surprising to find yourself studying as a mature student. The sense of achievement is extraordinary and I consider myself privileged to work in healthcare. I think my dad would have approved and I hope that my mum will have the benefit of my experience to help her as we navigate her experience of older age.

The Road to Apathy Is Paved with Unfortunate Souls
Joe McClaine

As the lights reflect over most of the small street, a beautiful low-lit blue, he has no idea that what he is going to find will change his view on reality. He is so naïve. He is yet to truly understand.

The door is opened by a young woman, and he immediately wonders if she's a mother. It's clear she's taken a beating; blood is escaping from a cut on her head and her nose is bleeding. Her face stained with tears, and she is still crying. She lets him and his seasoned mentor through the door. She takes a seat on the sofa. The older policeman takes charge, asks what has happened and where her husband is. She says she doesn't know, that he's gone out to calm down because he went into a fit of rage. She doesn't understand why. She never does.

Suddenly she bolts upright, rigid and strong, as if a thought has come into her mind. She shakes and looks panicked. She wants her daughter, and she has no idea where she has gone. The teenage policeman volunteers to go upstairs and look for her. He checks room by room, but there's no sign of her. The last room is the one with the pink door. He knows he should have checked this one first and berates himself for not doing so.

He opens the door but can't see anyone. He knows where to look, because it's where he would hide if he was scared. He looks under the bed and finds her. She's young and she's crying, but he tries to convince her of what he is not really convinced of himself. "You're going to be all right. You'll be safe with me. No one is going to hurt you," he assures her.

As she stands up, she grabs hold of his leg and hugs it tightly. He doesn't know what to do. Fighting back tears, he takes her by the hand, leads her down the stairs and into the protective arms of her mother.

A few hours later, he walks to the bus stop. It's raining, still dark, and the streets are deserted. He gets on the bus and sits at the back. He looks around, checking that no one else is there, that no one else might see. As he recalls the evening, something he knows he will never be able to forget, he puts his hood up and starts to cry silently. He tries to stop but he can't. The sound of the child's cries, the feeling of her tight grip won't ever leave him.

"Every time we turn our heads the other way, when we tolerate what we know to be wrong, when we close our eyes and ears to the corrupt because we are too busy or too frightened, when we fail to speak up and we fail to speak out, we strike a blow against freedom, decency and justice."

~ Robert F Kennedy

Ten years feels like a life time. It has all moved so quickly. He is older now and remembers how he used to feel. He used to be so idealistic and so positive. He used to believe that there was good in everyone. This moment in his life taught him what he now knows for certain—that he's not able to help everyone and that sometimes he will be helpless. This he will never forget.

A Baby and A Flood
Phyllis Betts

It was December, 1978 when I came out of hospital after having pneumonia. I was expecting my second child, Becky, but there were no signs of the baby arriving and I was feeling much better. This was before Christmas, and we had been having bad rain storms.

I lived in a caravan on the site in Gunthorpe with Bill, my husband, and Melanie, my eldest daughter, who was fourteen years old, but Melanie was staying with her dad when I came home from my stay in the hospital.

The caravan site was at the bottom of a very steep road, so you had to go down a deep dip to get in or out. The site, and Gunthorpe village in general, often flooded. This was the last of the really bad floods, so they say, when the area all around the caravan site and pub in the village was flooded.

Because of the floods, the police used to come around in boats several times a day to check that everyone was okay. We had no phones in those days to ask for help. On two occasions I had felt these twinges, and although they weren't really contractions, the boat took me out of the caravan and then helped me up to the ambulance on the top road. On both occasions the ambulance men stopped before we got to the hospital and took me back home, as the twinges had stopped.

When they fetched me the third time for the real thing it was night time. Getting into the boat was terrifying because I can't swim, and it was frosty and freezing cold, but I was well wrapped up in blankets. There were two men, one rowing, and as it was night time it was pitch black. I bet not many women have been taken away in a rowboat while they were in labour!

I eventually got to hospital and can remember the ambulance men saying to me, "Are we taking you all the way there this time, Phyllis?"

I was twenty-three hours in labour with Becky and in those days they made you stay in hospital for ten days after you'd given birth. Someone was able to tell my oldest daughter, Mel, about the baby arriving and she came into hospital to see me with the biggest bunch of red roses. Mel always loved roses.

"What are you doing here?" I asked her. "You're supposed to be at your dad's!"

"You're more important than being at Dad's," she replied.

I was worried about her being able to afford the roses, but she said that Dad had lent her money.

By the time we went home the floods had receded and Bill was able to fetch me in the car. No boat was required to bring my new daughter home.

It's My Life
Tina Barnes

One of my earliest childhood memories is going with my mum on the bus to the big building with a funny smell and a rocking horse that was too big for me to go on. I was three or four years old. The building was the QMC hospital. We had to go there a lot. That day, we were there for lots of different people to look at me and listen to my heart for their student doctor exams. I had to have lots of blood tests which I didn't like, and a test where they stuck these funny suckers on you which left red circles on your chest, an ECG, which made a funny picture of your heart beating, with lines going up and down.

You see, I was different from other boys and girls my age, as I had a special heart.

My story really started on March 21st, 1975, thirteen months before I was born when my mum suffered a stillbirth and lost my big brother, Kevin. Mum told us Kevin had been a very active baby, always kicking her. Then they told her they wanted to stick a needle in her belly to test some fluid from the sac around the baby in the womb. An amniocentesis. Kevin was stillborn. My mum was devastated.

Then in August she found out she was pregnant with me. She was scared because of what had happened with Kevin. Then my auntie told her she was pregnant as well and due the same day, which helped my mum through it as they had been pregnant at the same time together before. They monitored Mum more this time and on 30th April 1976 at 12:12 a.m. I was born (my Auntie Jo had a healthy baby boy one hour earlier). Mine was a healthy delivery and everything seemed fine, but my mum knew something wasn't right before we even left the hospital, as I would go grey and clammy. But she was told I was fine and to take me home.

Once I was home I would sleep lots and Mum had to wake me for feeds. But by the time I'd had one feed it was time for the next one. My mum knew this wasn't right, as I had an older sister, Sharon, so she kept taking me to the doctors and the old Children's Hospital, to explain that I was turning blue and clammy, and I wasn't even waking up to feed. They said nothing was wrong and to take me home. They put it down to postnatal depression from her losing Kevin. Plus, I never went grey or clammy when she took me there!

I had a hole on the outside of my left ear which needed an operation to close it. When having pre-op tests for the anaesthetic the doctor said I had a heart murmur. They carried out the operation and my mum was, like, "Really?! We've only been telling you from day one something was wrong and I'm not imagining it." As a result, I was sent to Groby Road, the hospital at Leicester to see Dr Goldberg. He thought it was PFO, patent foramen ovale, a hole in the heart. So at nine months old I was taken to surgery to close it. But when they opened me up, they saw it wasn't that. It was something much more complicated, so they closed me up and told my mum the next twenty-four hours were critical, if I made it. Obviously I did, and she took me home two weeks later.

I progressed well and at eighteen months I was taken in for another operation where they closed off some of the arteries because they said I looked like Spaghetti Junction. They told Mum I had something called pulmonary atresia with ventricular septal defect (VSD). Basically, that meant the valve that allowed blood to flow through my heart was blocked, and there was a hole between the two chambers that pump blood.

It must have been hard on my mum and dad, who didn't have a car so had to rely on buses everywhere. Plus, my mum never left me, which meant when I was in hospital she had to leave Sharon with my dad or granny.

By now I was coming up to school age and the next fight was to get me into a normal school. We had to see a psychologist but all they wanted to know about was my toileting rather than my learning. This really pissed my mum off and she told them we were there to check my head, not my bum. I got into normal school. The big day arrived and I was excited as my big sister was there as well. But I could only do a couple of hours in the morning or afternoon as any more was too much for me and I'd fall asleep. I had some lovely teachers. In winter they'd just open the doors up for me in the morning to let me in, and not the other kids, so I didn't get cold.

I remember Mum picking me up from school one day and telling me she had a secret. I was so excited; she told me I was going to be a big sister! So life was okay. I just had to go now and then to Groby Road for cardiac catheters to monitor me, but that seemed normal to me. My mum had my baby brother, Wayne, and I loved doing everything for him.

Then one day when I was about seven, I started going blue and clammy again and getting breathless. We were coming home from shopping and we were going up a hill, and my mum had to ask Wayne to get out and walk so I could go in his buggy.

I was about eight, and me and Mum were back at

Groby Road as I needed another operation. I can remember when Sharon and Wayne came to visit me in hospital. To stop Wayne, who was three, from jumping all over me, we showed him my stitches on my back. He asked, "Who did that?" So we told him the nurses and the doctors did to make me better. Then before anyone could stop him he was out in the corridor kicking the shin of a lovely student nurse who was walking down. "That's for hurting my Nina." (Because he couldn't say Tina.)

I returned to school but I still went a purple colour in the summer and blue in the cold so the other kids picked on me. They made comments about my colour saying, "You're an alien." I participated in some PE but the other kids would see my scars when I was in my vest and start whispering and chanting mean things. The teachers told the other kids to explain to them that I only had half a heart and that I was special.

After that the other kids would shout, "Half-a-heart, half-a-heart, you're going to die."

I hated it. I felt humiliated and small. I couldn't help it. To me, living this way was the norm. None of my family called me mean things, so why would my friends? I couldn't understand it.

I could just about cope with the name calling normally, but now I was ten and needed another operation and when it came up to hospital time the teasing really got to me. I'd been called things all day at school and was outside playing in my own garden when the lad next door started.

"Half-a-heart, you're going to die," he chanted.

I told him to shut up and went inside crying to my mum and dad. My mum marched round and spoke to his mum.

She said, "What do you expect? Kids will be kids." But she forced him to say a fake "sorry."

I was still upset so when I came in, my dad told me that if he said that again to call him "four eyes." So, the next day at school this lad starts teasing me again with his friends. I did what my dad said and called him "four eyes." Well, we both got sent to the head mistress who then had a go at me and said he couldn't help wearing glasses. She said I shouldn't tease him, and it wasn't a nice thing to do. It was so unfair and I was mad!

I turned around and said, "I can't help having heart trouble."

To which she responded, "Well, if you didn't eat so many sweets and chocolate you wouldn't have heart trouble."

I was that upset that I ran home and told my mum, who dumped Wayne with a neighbour and stormed up to the school. She was really pissed off and had it out with the teacher,who backed down. My mum gave me a hug. She was my hero.

And so, at ten, I had my next operation. The first frontal one where they break your rib cage open. I knew Mr Bailey, the surgeon, well by then, and I said I wouldn't let him operate on me in the new green coloured scrubs. So he found his old orange ones, which I preferred, and then he saved an orange set just for me. Groby Road was a strange hospital, as it was all old army barracks, and I can still remember the smell of the dinner trolley, which was hard when you were nil-by-mouth.

The operation was very painful and I remember being so self-conscious as my chest was starting to develop. This time in hospital we met a lovely couple who were in the Forces and their new born daughter needed an emergency heart operation right away. My mum reassured this other new mum because her husband couldn't get there to be with her, and my mum knew how helpless and scared she felt. I remember watching and thinking how proud I was of my mum and how much I loved her and how strong she was. And I thought this lady could believe my mum when she said everything would be okay because Mum was always right and everything was always okay. That couple bought me a little teddy which I called Alistair after one of the fit doctors I had a crush on, and I've still got him thirty-two years later. I took him to all my operations for good luck.

*

Life moved on and I started secondary school. We had moved house in the meantime so I didn't know anybody at school, even my sister wasn't there. The school was up a big hill so I was short of breath before I even got there. I only did three days before I was back in for my next operation. Those were the only three days of school I did that year. Mr Bailey did the successful operation. It had taken longer than expected so he had to rush off to catch a plane as he was going off teaching abroad. A colleague finished stitching me back up. A couple of days later while they were checking me, Mum noticed I was getting pressure sores and the stitches on my back were starting to open.

Dr Lennigee said not to worry. "It's just a little hole." He instructed the nurses to use steri strips.

But it burst open even more, and two lots of stitches came apart. The wound was six inches long and gaping open. You'd think it would be agony, but I didn't feel any more pain than before it split open.

Another doctor, who was just back from America, had seen them packing open wounds with ordinary caster sugar to keep them clean. So from the next day, twice a day, that's what we did. I could tell everyone was worried and something was up as everyone was being overly nice

to me. Every day, my mum bathed me at the hospital. She
had stuck paper towels over the mirror and had written "do
not remove" on them so I wouldn't see how bad it was. I
felt an itch on my back while I was in the bath and reached
round and was horrified when my fingers went deep into
the wound. Mum patted me dry and as I turned to look at
her with my arm stretched up I caught sight of my gaping
wound in the mirror, as the cleaners had removed the paper
towels my mum had put up so I wouldn't see it. I freaked
and ran off crying with a towel wrapped around me and
locked myself, sobbing, in a toilet. My mum was in pieces
outside and kept apologising to me, even though it wasn't
her fault.

Eventually, I was re-stitched with one hundred and
fifty stitches outside and I don't know how many inside
and spent a total of three months in hospital. I'd had renal
failure as well. By then I was so miserable my dad brought
in my own quilt and food from home. Unknown to me, my
mum and dad negotiated a weekend's leave for my twelfth
birthday as I was so fed up. We all went to the Savoy Hotel
for dinner, birthday cake and everything. That felt really
special.

We'd asked about the possibility of a heart transplant
when I was eleven but were laughed at. Then at fourteen
we received a letter from Dr Qureshi at Guy's Hospital
in London. He was a heart specialist who wanted to do
more investigations with cardiac catheters to see what he
might be able to do, and he even mentioned looking at
the possibility of a heart and lung transplant after all. But
that never happened. Before the catheter operation I'd
been nil by mouth all day and was waiting for a paediatric
anaesthetist. They kept saying to wait, and that they were
finding one.

I was on the kids' ward although I was fourteen or
fifteen. We called Dr Qureshi by his first name, Shakeel,

which we shortened to Shak. About 7:30 p.m. Shak came in and said they couldn't get an anaesthetist, so it wasn't going to happen. Then he ordered a big Chinese for me, him, and my mum then told me to get off the bed because he needed a lie down as he'd been busy all day and I'd been lying in bed all day. He chatted to my mum until about one in the morning. No words can say how amazing a bloke he is.

Dr Qureshi asked if we would be interested in taking part in some filming of my next operation. We thought at first it was for teaching students but it turned out to be a BBC QED documentary. We agreed and had camera crews turn up at the house (which Mum had redecorated especially for the filming). They followed us around town and they even came on holiday to Cumbria with us. And they filmed my next heart surgery. When it was shown on the telly, one of my school teachers videoed it and showed it at school in PSHE lessons. So all the children from first to fifth year got to see it.

I thought it might help people understand my illness but it had the opposite effect and I got another round of teasing and bullying. The film showed where a catheter was inserted into my shaved groin as part of my surgery.

Kids at school just laughed. "We've seen your bald bits on the telly," and "Have you not even hit puberty yet?"

It was cruel and humiliating. I know it was on TV but it felt wrong that the teacher thought she had the right to show it to everyone in my school. I was so mad and upset. It was all I could do to get up the two flights of stairs to the classroom where she was showing it. I was out of breath and tried to get her to turn it off but she said I didn't have the right to and besides, it had been on the telly. She switched it off but my brother's friend told me she put it back on after I'd gone.

At about that age I'd started taking diuretics (water

tablets) for my kidneys. So when I needed a wee I really needed to go. I'd put my hand up in class to go to the loo but by the time I was back I needed to go again. The teacher wouldn't let me go because I'd just been and thought I was messing about. So I had accidents. I felt humiliated and wanted to just curl up under a rock as other kids teased me. I took spare clothes to school with me every day but you couldn't clean up properly.

I finished school and went to college, but it was too much so I had to give it up. I got on with life, just going into hospital now and then for catheters so they could monitor things and stretch arteries if they needed doing.

In 2008, I went for a routine catheter. I'd been a bit more breathless and the cyanosis (blue-grey colouring) was worse. I was down there for quite a while and my mum asked what was going on. They took her down to theatre where Shak was apologising and saying sorry to her because there was blood all over the floor. Mum told me later she thought I'd gone, what with Shak apologising and the blood and everything. When the catheter came out of my groin, because of all the scar tissue from previous ones, he tore a main artery as he pulled it out.

The next day when I was up on the ward—you had to lay flat on your back for twelve hours after a catheter—I asked for the commode. I got on it okay, I got off it okay, and then I just had a tiny cough and the wound burst open again and blood spurted everywhere. The nurse threw me on the bed, tipped it up and pushed her fist in my groin. They found a huge blood clot which they decided to try and disperse by injecting it with ten big needles full of Heparin. I asked if they could numb the area first but they said they couldn't. It was agony. My toes and fingers were clenched as they shoved the ultrasound probe into my groin to see where to put the needles in. I was clenching my mum's hand and thinking, how does anyone give birth to kids?

In June we got the results from that catheter from Shak. Me, Mum, and Sharon and the kids had a family day down to London. He told me that he couldn't do anything else for me and thinks I've got something else, and I should go to Papworth in Cambridge for tests. I'd been seeing him for eighteen years. He was like a family friend. I was gutted. We had a few tears, and he hugged me and said he'd make sure I was seen by only the best. So off to Papworth we went for lung function tests. When the results came back they said Pulmonary Hypertension, a rare lung condition with no cure. They spoke about maybe a double heart and lung transplant but because of what's missing in my heart and how rare my condition is, I wouldn't be a suitable candidate. It wouldn't be straight forward. I had already said I didn't want one anyway because they could save three people with those organs. I saw the heart specialist, Doctor Fisher, who Shak had trained, so that gave me confidence.

So now I go there every three to six months for tests and checks. In November, 2008, I was put on oxygen at night. Now I've deteriorated that much over the last few years that there's nothing more medically they can do for me.

So about five years ago I asked my mum if she'd come with me to arrange my funeral.

She said, "Don't be daft. Don't be daft."

I felt bad asking her but it was just something I wanted to do for them, if that makes sense. To take that burden off them. In the end she did and we sorted it all out.

I arranged a DNR (do not resuscitate) order to be put in place. I ended up in hospital last year for six months with fluid in the heart and lungs. I was on really strong diuretics and they think I had a TIA, a mild stroke. I knew because the heart monitor kept flat-lining, my hands locked, and my face went funny. I was bricking it. I was on my own as my mum had gone to get a coffee. When she came back she took one look at me and the monitor and said, "I'll be back in a minute," and rushed off to get the nurses. Blood tests showed I'd had a stroke. I told them that if I was dying I wanted to go home. So as soon as the medicine finished, I was home.

I've been told I'm "end of life." I've got wonderful tablets at home for strong pain relief if I need them. I'm on oxygen 24/7 and confined to a wheelchair. I'm not meant to be walking because it's too much pressure on my heart.

You know, when I was little I always used to think, I don't want to play this game anymore, and wished Wayne or Sharon were ill instead. But now I just want to keep them all safe and don't want to hurt them. So I'm still fighting to be here, and I'll go down fighting. And if I had to live this life again I wouldn't do anything different. I'd live the same life over and over and over again as long as I had my mum, dad, brother, and sister beside me. I can't put into words how much I love my family and how proud I am of them for how brave they've been in supporting me on my journey.

Our Journey: My Letter to Tina
Heather Barnes

It started back in August 1975. I was thrilled to be pregnant again. Then fear and panic kicked in, big time, as in March 1975, I gave birth to my first son, Kevin, but that didn't have a happy ending. Due to hospital negligence, Kevin was stillborn at full term. I never saw my son. I never held him, and this pain has never left me.

I had the thought, "What if it happens again? I couldn't do it."

Then your Auntie Jo said, "Guess what? I'm pregnant and due the same day."

How we laughed, as we'd been pregnant together before when I had your sister, Sharon. This took my mind off things a bit, plus the hospital had said they would be monitoring me closely. I spent a lot of time at the hospital, never given a reason why, and was just told there was nothing for me to worry about. They just didn't want a repeat of what had happened with my son.

Well, the big day arrived. I was taken down to the labour suite to be induced at eight a.m. At 12:12 p.m. on the 30th April, 1976, you made your entrance. A safe delivery and one healthy little girl. For a few minutes, I wished you'd been a boy, but once I held you, all those thoughts disappeared.

I was just glad you were safe and sound. Next up: what

name do we give you? I know I had wanted to call Sharon, Katrina, but for some reason your dad chose Sharon. So Katrina was shortened to Tina, which proved to be the right name: T for Trouble!

At first everything seemed okay but then doubt started to rear its ugly head. *Please, no. Don't do this to me again.* I had mentioned to the nurse that you had this funny colour and struggled to suck your bottles. And you seemed clammy, always making your bedding damp, but they just ignored me, saying that all babies do this for a few days. *Okay, who am I to say anything different?*

When we went home, things didn't improve. When the Health Visitor came by six weeks later, things were still the same, and I was convinced something was wrong. I'm your mum. I just know. But she didn't think anything was wrong. She thought that I had postnatal depression starting and that I would benefit from starting on tablets. I told her what she could do with those tablets!

Weeks turned into months with no change, and I was constantly talking to doctors and the children's hospital, hoping someone would listen to me properly. You didn't help as you never did any of the things I was complaining about when we were there, and because otherwise, your development was normal. They'd try to reassure me that you were fine, that the problem was me, and that I needed counselling.

At around six or seven months, you needed a small operation on your ear. It was during these tests for anaesthetics that the doctor noted he could hear a heart murmur. Hoorah, I'm not a mad woman. So this is when our journey began and what a journey it's been.

The doctor asked me why this hadn't been mentioned before. I explained that I had constantly been talking to the doctors, but they said I was suffering from postnatal depression and I wasn't taken seriously.

Things moved very quickly from here, with a referral made to Groby Road Hospital in Leicester, which was a cardiac unit. You saw a Dr Goldberg, who diagnosed you with a very common complaint, PDA, which stands for Patent Ductus Arteriosus. This ductus should close within the first few days after birth. Yours didn't.

They suggested surgery with it being a simple procedure. Everything was arranged to get you in as soon as possible with you having problems since birth. "REALLY? So I'm not a twenty-year-old neurotic mum."

You were booked in for your operation when the letter came. I felt physically sick with all sorts going through my head: what you needed for the hospital, where I would stay as we didn't drive then, and the bus only ran every hour. And we had no family support either, and I didn't want to leave you there alone. Soon though, things started to fall into place, and the day arrived for your admission.

Groby Road was an old hospital spread out in beautiful gardens, and they put me in the nurse's room, which was a huge relief. We met Dr Goldberg and Mr. Bailey, who were doing your operation. It was planned for the following day. The day was busy with you having all sorts of tests before surgery. That night I was unable to sleep. My mind was racing around doing all sorts. Morning came. I bathed you in pre-op soap and put your theatre gown on. My heart was racing every time a nurse walked passed. I felt sick. The porters came to collect you, and I wasn't able to go with you to the theatre block. I gave you the biggest hug and kisses, and off you went at eight a.m.

I was told you would be a couple of hours, so I should go and have a bath and relax for a bit. They said if I was needed, they would fetch me. After four hours, there was no sign of you. The staff kept saying they hadn't heard anything. By now, I was scared stiff. I couldn't move with fear. I tried to have some dinner but couldn't, due to feeling so sick. So I just stayed in the children's playroom watching *Sons and Daughters*.

At last, Dr Goldberg arrived on the ward eight hours after you'd been taken to surgery. I looked at the nurse's face and I knew something was seriously wrong. He asked me to sit down, then he started to say that things hadn't worked out as planned, and that you were in critical condition. He told me that if you made it through the next twenty-four hours, we'd be very lucky.

My head exploded. What was he saying? "NO, NOT MY TINA. NOT MY BABY." He had it all wrong—he had to have. He said that he would speak to me again tomorrow. I told him I didn't want to hear any more rubbish. "How could she be this ill when, for nine months, I was told I was an over-reacting mum?" We were told that sometimes things like this can happen, but for some unknown reason, it can be hard to diagnose.

I was taken to the ITU to see you. Oh my God, how I cried. You looked so small covered in wires and tubes, with machines bleeping, and your chest all stitched up. I sat by your side all night, only leaving you to get a drink part way through the night. I just needed to get out for some fresh air. I wandered around the hospital grounds, freezing, as it was January. I found myself in the small chapel. I prayed, cursing that if there was a God, he should prove it so I didn't lose my baby. He'd already taken my son.

You remained stable all night and the staff said you were doing a lot better than they expected. They suggested that I went and got some sleep as when you woke, you'd need me. We went home after two and a half weeks. Life became stable and normal, and you carried on growing and developing like any other child.

*

Over the next five years you remained in good health with just a few blips. It was time for you to start school. What a headache that was. They felt that it would be better for you to attend a "special" school. *Over my dead body.*

So we started a new journey. Endless visits to see a child psychologist to assess you. This idiot naffed me off big time. All he seemed interested in was your bowel movements. After about the fourth visit, he started again about your bowels. In the end I said that I thought we had come to assess your ability to manage in a normal school, not your bottom that doesn't learn anything. We walked out, never to return again.

From that day, I became a different mum. You're my daughter, why should you be treated any different? So, no more. You are Tina, my brave and strong warrior. I was never going to let anyone or anybody humiliate you ever again. You went to normal school, and I don't think that the psychologist dared suggest anything else.

You loved school, although you found the days long and you would just fall asleep anywhere. You developed the same as your class mates, and the only thing you couldn't do was games.

Life has never been boring. We've had a lot of heartache and fun on this journey so far, and I'd earned a reputation of a bullish mother who challenged everyone in authority.

Then, when you were about six years old, you started to show signs that things weren't right. Your colour had gone from a pinky-blue to blue-grey all the time. You had become more tired and were sleeping more. Back we went to Groby Road to see a new doctor.

He felt that he could do some corrective surgery, but it would be a big operation with a high risk. He explained you had lots of collaterals supplying your blood but he felt they needed closing, as you were getting too much blood to your heart and lungs. This was putting too much pressure on your heart to be able to work normally.

So once again, off we went. This operation was a sort of a success. You were in surgery for eight hours and then taken to ITU (intensive treatment unit). They had managed to close some off, but not all was as it seemed. They had found other problems which they felt needed more investigation.

When I saw you, you were pink again with just blue nails. Again, we went home and everything continued to improve.

Eight months after your operation, we received a letter from the hospital and they wanted to see you again. They'd been studying your tests and information from your last surgery. You went in for catheterisation for them to gain extra information. This went okay, and from this they decided to have a go at correcting your heart.

A date was set for your last operation. As we thought, you went into surgery, but this time things didn't feel right. I didn't feel right, but I had to be strong for you. Ten hours in surgery seemed like a life time. I was thinking to myself, *Will it ever end?* But it did. Yet again, things had gone wrong, and they hadn't managed to correct you. Whilst you were in ITU, things started to go wrong straight away. You weren't responding as you usually did. Three days in and your scar started to open. It went black, then it just busted open. Layers of stitches had just gone. From under your arm around up to your shoulder, it was wide open. You also had pressure sores on your heels and forehead where your ventilator had been. I just kept thinking, *What else can happen?*

Because the surgeon was away and because of infection, you couldn't be re-stitched. To keep the wound clean, it was packed twice a day with normal caster sugar. A surgeon had just returned from America, and this was something he said they used to great effect.

You slowly improved, only to take a step back. You had problems with your kidneys. It was as if you had given up.

Eventually, the time came for them to re-stitch your back, but you still remained very poorly. It was coming up to your birthday so as a surprise, the hospital allowed us to bring you home for the day. This did you the world of good. It gave you something to focus on and get better.

The day finally came for us to go home after three agonising months. Once home you continued to go from strength to strength. Leicester contacted us and said they had been talking to a Dr Qureshi at Guy's in London. They said he'd like to meet us and take over your care.

This was a new adventure and a bloody long journey. So, off we went.

When we met Dr Qureshi, he made you feel at home. We spoke about all what you'd been through, and he reassured us he would only do what he thought was best for you and not put you through anything unnecessary.

We started by having a cardiac catheter, as they were less invasive than open heart surgery. And by now, you'd had five operations done at Leicester and London.

You had about six catheters, and the doctors thought they could do one more final operation to correct you. This operation took nearly a year to organise. The reason for this was it was to be the first of its kind, and Dr Qureshi had designed this equipment, but it was being made in America so there were a lot of legal issues around it, and it had to have clearance before the operation could take place.

The call came from Guy's to go and see Dr Qureshi. At this meeting, everything was explained to us. There was a very serious risk involved as this was basically an experiment. If it worked, there'd be no reason why you couldn't live a normal life, so we decided to go ahead.

During all this time, we talked with you, explaining

everything. This is something I felt was important from a very early age. You've always been involved and had everything explained to you so you could understand what was happening. If you'd said no at any time, I would've respected your wishes.

While we waited for the equipment to be made, life had continued as normal.

Until one day when Dr Qureshi rang us. I asked if they were ready for us.

"No, not yet. But I was just wondering if we could film Tina's operation?"

"Yeah, why not if it's going to help medical students."

A couple of days later we got another phone call.

"Hello, Mrs Barnes. My name is David Singleton from the BBC. I believe Dr Qureshi has spoken to you about filming your daughter's forthcoming operation for QED?"

"What? You're joking! I thought he meant for student doctors, not the television."

He asked if that made a difference, and I said it didn't, so he asked about coming up to meet the family and you. We arranged for them to come up that Saturday.

I thought someone was playing a joke on us.

David came and explained what they had planned. He said he had a very difficult question to ask us: if anything bad happened, would we still allow them to show the program? We spoke as a family and decided that, should the unfortunate happen, we would allow the programme to be aired in honour of you. Plus a lot of hard work had gone into making the programme, and even if it failed for you, it might give other families in this situation the hope that it would work for them.

The day came, so off we went. The film crew met us at the hospital and started filming. It was quite funny as people thought we were actors. Ha!

The operation went ahead. It had a few hiccups, mostly

because the catheter was wrong, but they had gone too far to stop. The operation was a success and everyone was pleased.

We still went for regular checks and things remained good.

But yet again, it raised its ugly head. You were showing signs of problems, so off we went again for a catheter. This was to be your last one as during the catheter, they found you had now developed Pulmonary Hypertension. This catheter also had its problems. You wouldn't stop bleeding in theatre. When they took me to you, it looked like a blood bath. I've never felt so scared as I was the moment I walked into that theatre. My legs froze for a second. Then, remembering why they'd allowed me in there, for you, I thought, *Pull yourself together. Tina needs you.* And there was something in Dr. Qureshi's eyes I'd not seen before which scared me even more.

I remember my shoe was stuck in the dried blood when we had to move. You'd developed a massive embolism in your groin. You'd just got out of bed to use the toilet when blood shot out everywhere. It scared me to death. I thought, *Oh, my God, all that we've been through with her heart and I'm going to lose her to a haemorrhage.* Your colour just drained. Bless you, you had to have needles stuck in the embolism to dissolve it or it would mean surgery again.

Dr Qureshi came to break the news of your hypertension. He said he was so sorry that it had to end this way, but he was referring you to Papworth, which in his opinion was the best, and if you were his daughter, this was where he'd want you to go.

Over the years he had become a friend and not just your doctor. We had some great laughs with him. You were always winding him up about being late and you once bought him a Bart Simpson alarm clock. He did laugh, and even now, he still asks after you. How lovely is that? He was brilliant, and I will always have a lot of respect for him. He saved your life and gave you extra time, for which I will always be grateful. How do you thank someone for that? Words just don't seem enough.

When we were referred to Papworth I thought that they would come up with something positive but instead it was totally the opposite. They explained there was no cure for this disease and unfortunately you wouldn't be considered for a transplant, as this would need to be a double transplant heart/lung. This was because of you having so many open heart surgeries and having bad scar tissue. Also, because your anatomy isn't normal it meant they would be unable to make the connection match. Doctors have always said that your plumbing is complicated. And transplants aren't always the answer, as you are still on medication to stop rejection and at any time you could reject the organ.

People are always asking me, "How do you cope? You never show any weakness." She's my daughter. What do you thing I'm going to do, walk away?

Well, here goes, after spending years in the care of the Local Authority you had to learn to survive or sink. The care system never broke me; I broke them by not becoming one of their statistics so I wasn't about to let this break me or my daughter. You deserved better than that.

*

So maybe this is why I find it hard to show emotion. Don't get me wrong, I'm not a heartless mum. But my feelings are buried very deep so as not to be hurt. I have to be strong for Tina and the rest of my family; I'm the back bone that holds the family together. It's also very hard to show emotion as I have built this brick wall which nothing can penetrate.

I have also been scared that if I showed I wasn't coping

with this situation then the local authority would step in.
Over my dead body.

Yes, I'm hurting with so much pain and fear that I
sometimes wish I could just run away and have my own
time. This doesn't mean Tina is a burden and never has
or will be. It's just that it's so hard to remain positive to
everyone all the time when I just want someone to hold me
and tell me it's all going to be okay. Which I know it's not.
(I said I don't show emotion, so why am I crying as I do this
bit?)

Plus, if I was weak it wouldn't help Tina to be positive
and to continue fighting the way she has over the years.
And I want to thank Sharon and Wayne for understanding
why I have had to spend so much of my time with Tina. I
know there have been times when they feel they have been
neglected but that hasn't stopped me worrying about them.
But I have always been there when needed, and that will
never change, as I love all my children with all my heart.
I'm so sorry, Sharon and Wayne, for not always being there
for you.

I want to mention my husband, Bill. He is my rock
and was always by my side or at the end of a phone when
we were away in hospital. It wasn't always possible for
him to be with Tina and me as we had to maintain a normal
environment for Sharon and Wayne (although they loved
being spoiled staying with their granny).

I would like to thank my beautiful, brave daughter,
Tina, for showing me the special side to being a mum and
keeping me on my toes. It's been a privilege to accompany
you on your journey. You've always faced everything life
has thrown at you with that beautiful smile, and you never
moaned—well, maybe a little, but you were entitled to do
so with everything you have overcome. You make my heart
beat with so much pride. Thank you, my brave warrior.

Being a Longhorn
Ron Gascoigne

When I was a little lad, about eight or nine years old, my father used to work at AVRO repairing Vulcan Bombers at Langar airfield. He had a bad accident and he ended up with four metal plates in his legs, so work was non-existent for him. So to help out I started mowing lawns at people's houses to earn a shilling. At that time it was a lot of money, at least, it was to us. When no lawns needed mowing we used to climb up into the woods and pick bluebells and sell them for a penny.

When I was younger I used to be a bit short and scrawny. At the age of sixteen I caught the bus to work every day. I would sit about half way down, and I noticed these two girls sitting at the front of the bus, but I never spoke to them. I wanted to but never dared say a word. They were always already on the bus when I got on. As time went on one of the girls used to give me a crafty little wave as I got off the bus before her. It got to the point where I would get on the bus in the morning even when I wasn't going to work.

I wasn't dating at the time and my sister's boyfriend used to constantly ask me to go out on a date with his sister, Pat. Eventually I said I would go just to shut them up and a date was arranged for Saturday night at the Railway Club in Nottingham for a dance night. On the day, she came to the house with her brother and as I came down the stairs, shaking like a leaf, there was this girl I'd seen on the bus. I said to her, "You're that girl on the bus! I'm the scrawny little bugger who sits half way down!"

We had only been going out for three weeks when we were sat on the wall outside the Railway Club and she said to me, "What would you say if I asked you to marry me?" "I'd say yes." Then I said to her, "Have I got to go and talk to your dad?" and she said, "No, I've already told him!" We went into town the next Saturday to buy the ring and so we technically got engaged sitting on the front seat of the number 38 tram. We ended up having a double wedding (my sister married Pat's brother) and have been married for over fifty years now. We've always done everything together, including the fundraising I'd been passionate about since I was young lad.

I more or less helped out with anything as I was growing up, and when I was older I joined a group called the Longhorns. They met at our local pub, the Cavendish Arms in Carlton. I got to know the compère/singer there and one night he introduced me to the Longhorns, who were just a group of people who used to get together to raise money, collecting mainly for children's charities. There was always a tin going around for something or other, and I jumped in with both feet.

I can remember one little lad in Nottingham who only had one arm. There was just about every charity in Nottingham involved in raising money for a "bionic arm." There was so much money involved that they had enough to set up a trust fund. The little lad was able to use this money, and the interest helped him to keep having replacement limbs as he got older and grew.

When Queens Medical Centre opened we decided to raise money for the children's wards for the children who had to stay in over Christmas. We had so much donated that I virtually filled the lounge of the pub with all the gifts. We went in to hand out the presents and guess who had to dress up as Santa? On Christmas morning I was there, beard and all, and it was great to take the presents around the wards, just to see the kids' faces light up. But then I had to go into Intensive Care and I can remember one little lad who hadn't long to live. I went in but had to cover my clothes with a protective gown and such. Later, when the nurse came out to tell me that he died, I was absolutely devastated.

We must have raised thousands of pounds over the years, but sadly the group is no longer running as there aren't many of us still around. Recently, I went down to the summer fair at the Hospice with my wife, and we brought along one of those tamper proof money tins to raise funds. I said to my wife, Pat, "What are you going to do with that money?" and she said, "Why don't we give it to the Hospice?" We raised about seventy pounds that day and the Hospice gave me a certificate at Christmas to say thank you.

I just feel that everyone needs a helping hand at some point in their lives, and I've always felt that. If anyone says to me that they have a problem, within minutes I'll have worked out a way around the problem. The only thing I ask in return is that whoever receives the money would write a letter to say thank you, so that it can be pinned up on the wall for everyone to see who has helped them.

I am more than willing to help raise money; even now I would like to participate in fundraising for the Hospice. If the Longhorns were still alive they would be raising thousands of pounds and carrying on with their fundraising. I'm glad I can continue doing it myself.

My Journey to Recovery
Malcom Corbett

The day I got diagnosed with a terminal illness in 2012 changed my life. It all started when, in late 2011, I started to experience the feeling of being bloated. This carried on until one day I could hardly move. My stomach felt so tender to the touch on the right side, under my rib cage. I started feeling lethargic and couldn't be bothered with anything. I hadn't worked for a number of years, but when the illness started I was home all the time. I couldn't go anywhere, do anything. I couldn't do housework or cook. It felt horrible not to be able to do things for myself, which angered me a lot. I'd always been very independent, and I became demoralized by having to rely on other people.

At that time I was drinking very heavily; up to nine litres of alcohol, the cheapest I could find.

I went to the doctor when I couldn't stand the pain and bloating anymore. He felt about my abdomen but couldn't find anything, and he said, "If it carries on, then come back."

So I went on and still the pain continued after about a week, but I just thought it would go away.

I left it. But as the days went by the pain became worse, so the doctor sent me to see a gastro specialist, where they took a sample of fluid from my stomach. It came out looking like mud and water. This was called acetic fluid.

I didn't know what that was at the time, but it concerned me because my liver wasn't working properly. I couldn't process the fluid and enzymes in my body. It came down to me not being able to process everything.

After, he told me to go home, and if I had any more problems to give them a call. A week went by and I was getting really tired due to not feeling like eating. I hadn't eaten properly for about a month. One day I called the specialist department because my stomach was feeling bloated again, and I had the same pain I'd had prior to going to see him the first time.

I ended up staying in the Gastro Ward for several days, due to my stomach bloating quite a bit. They drained it again, only two weeks after they'd drained it before.

The medical staff were great. I slept quite a bit because I knew that if anything was to happen, they'd be there. But I couldn't sleep due to not knowing what was going on with my body. I was constantly worried.

Instead of getting better, it became every couple of days I needed to be drained, so they decided to put me in for a scan.

I was nervous and crying, thinking I'm going to die.

That night was the change that made me give up drinking, which I was craving. I didn't want to die.

The scan wasn't good. They said, "Malcolm, we've got bad news. You have terminal liver cirrhosis."

Tears and shaking overcame me. I'd decided to stop drinking, but it was too late.

I knew it was bad, though, so it wasn't a huge shock.

A few days later, I got discharged.

They put in for carers to come in to help me with things around the house. The district nurse came and saw how low I was, so they made a referral for the Nottingham Hospice. It was a place for people with terminal illness…God, why me? I couldn't imagine being around old folk all the time.

My life was blank, and I decided to go and have a look. It wasn't as bad as I thought, though. There was laughter and a calming atmosphere. I liked it. I was going one day a week to see if I liked the place, then they put me down for two times a week.

Even though people were friendly and I liked it there, I kept myself to myself, not interacting and feeling self-pity without a thought for the others who were in a more serious category of illness.

As I felt so low, they asked a counsellor to speak to me to get my anger out, as I could no longer walk like I used to, and other circumstances were making me miserable.

He was fantastic from day one. Ian was a volunteer counsellor I saw once a week.

What a difference it made getting my anger out vocally.

Then my physical situation changed again. I started more trips to the hospital with my stomach bloating. Ian came up to see me and kept the nurses informed, as they always kept a good eye on me.

I was still drinking at that time, but I couldn't keep it down. I was just being sick, but I kept trying, sick or not. I kept crying all the time, night after night. I drank to help me deal with my emotions.

I wasn't eating. I looked frail and jaundiced. I was half the man I used to be. People didn't recognise me.

As the months went by there were more stays in hospital. I wasn't coping at home, I was letting my flat go into disrepair, and I wasn't bothering about my personal appearance. I simply didn't care about anything anymore.

I stopped going to the Hospice because I was being sick, not keeping any food or drink down, and I didn't feel like I could leave the house. But being on my own made me feel worse, and it made the depression worse. It felt like being in a glass coffin.

At this point I came down with a very bad infection

for which I was taken into hospital for three weeks. I had constipation along with the pain and bloating, and some of the pain was due to the feeling of not wanting to go to the toilet.

So they put a central line in the back of my neck (so the liquid form of antibiotics could get to work quicker). They said the site of the incision and tube hole had become infected, so they decided to take the drain out.

I was also getting pain in my kidney area, so the kidney specialist came in and we talked for a while, then they decided to send me for an ultrasound scan; but nothing showed up, and everything was fine.

They took the tube out of my side where the infection was, which hurt very much. It wouldn't stop bleeding, so they put a colostomy cover on it so the blood could go into it. I was put on drips of fluid, cut down to one litre due to the fluid build-up inside me, which wasn't easy because of the heat in the hospital.

I spent three weeks in there, and all the time the counsellor at the hospice came up and bought me pencils, paper, and something to nibble on (namely, biscuits).

Over the next three weeks I was improving...but when I got discharged the specialist said they didn't think I'd live through another three weeks.

They told me to come back two days after discharge so I could have a new pleural drain put in, and after about three weeks with it in, they decided to take it out, which was a blessing as having something attached to me was a pain.

Then, in 2014 summer time, when I was walking on the road I lived on, I tripped and fractured my pubic bone...total agony. But I didn't seek help for four days. I had a friend staying to help me as I didn't want to go in hospital in case I didn't come out.

Then came the day I knew I couldn't live with the pain any longer, and I told my friend to call 999. But at that moment the carer came, which was good as my friend couldn't get me up on his own.

Off I went to hospital. The paramedics gave me gas to ease the pain, and what a good feeling it was to not have the pain. Got to the hospital and into A&E. They sent me for a scan but couldn't really see anything, so I was in bed, just waiting for answers.

A few hours later they took me down for a scan, and this time I was just laying on a sheet with no mattress. They finally found something, but it was a hairline fracture. They couldn't do anything about it, I just had to rest and go to physio.

Then a few months passed and things were getting easier. Between the pain killers that actually managed my pain, and the counselling that was helping me deal with my emotions, life was changing. That was when I finally gave drink the push...it felt great after a few months, especially not waking up feeling groggy. The urge for the drink was just about gone, and my tobacco intake was reduced, too.

Then in 2015 I went back to the Nottinghamshire Hospice. People couldn't believe I was the same guy who nine months ago was at death's door.

I became more outgoing. I had a dark sense of humour when I got back to the Hospice, where I became close to a few patients. The worthiness of the Hospice should be recognized for the service they provide. The nursing staff, the drivers and the volunteers make the place a valuable part of my recovery. The Hospice is a place to relax and just be yourself. There are activities too, including trips out if the weather permits. I also just enjoy the Hospice atmosphere, which is calm and relaxed and helps you take your mind off your illness. I've been five years without a drink now, and I'm incredibly grateful.

Memories of a Broxtowe Boy
Gordon West

The first thing I remember was when I came out of the house in 1947. I was eight, and the snow was deeper than me. Everyone was out clearing the snow. I can remember the dustbin lorry; it had steel wheels instead of rubber. When it went around the corner it slid around it. On Denton Green there was a sign saying keep off the grass, but they didn't.

At the top of the road was a big air raid shelter. We had one in the back garden, too. I can only remember going in once. It was actually quite exciting to a little lad. We also had chickens and rabbits.

It was a good walk to John Player school, and they also had air raid shelters. It wasn't a mixed school, just boys back then. When the fog was bad the teacher would walk us home. At Christmas if you were poorly they would come to see you. When I started to be bullied I took up boxing, and I was okay after that. I also played rugby. No more bullying. A mate of mine who I knocked about with was called a lot before he left school (he was a really big lad). He went round all the bullies and gave them a right good bashing.

Facing the school, the road was called Chingford. At the back of the shops was the gypsies, parked up. They made clothes pegs, carving them with a knife. Further on you came to Beechdale Road which was laid by German POWs. As a matter of fact, the Italian POWs planted the trees at Moorgreen Woods. One of the teachers used to put pink petrol in his car; you could smell it a mile away. It was illegal. I don't know where they got it from. I never had any decent clothes, and I had to put cardboard in my shoes. It was the 1950's and Macmillan said we'd never had it so good. It might've been like that for some folk, but it wasn't like that for me.

I went into the military at seventeen and a half for three years. We were stationed at Oswestry. There is a church there made of marble in remembrance of Canadians killed in Dieppe. My favourite place was Cyprus, and I was there for eighteen months.

In 1959, I came out of the army. I met Val on a blind date at the Palais (revolving floor). We were married that year. You know what blokes are like; her dad didn't know how old she was. He said if he had, he wouldn't have let us marry. She had just turned seventeen, and I was still in the army (we've been married for fifty-seven years). We sold our terraced house for £350 and bought a bungalow for £2,250. A lot of money in them days!

I had a moped (NSU) then a motorbike and sidecar until I got a car. Married life was good but it was hard. But I wouldn't change a thing. Since I've had this illness, I've had some wonderful people who have gone that extra mile to help. And my wife has kept me going. Over three years ago they said I only had six months. I've done well.

Gordon West did his best,
And still had to go like the rest.
He thought he was the best,
But he was a pest.

Dreaming
Yvonne Dunning

Nottingham, 1971

I watched Mum take her last breath. The pained expression relaxed and she was finally free. The tears began to flow, but more from relief than sadness. What a relief to see her free from pain. A burden was lifted. I had forgotten how it was to be a normal teenager; perhaps I could be one now. I had cared for her for many hours, day and night, for months. And constantly for the last two weeks.

All of the family had been in the kitchen for about the last four hours, getting drunk to drown their sorrows. It seemed that I didn't exist; no-one asked if I was all right as I sat alone in the front room just watching Mum. It now seemed obvious that everyone had known she was dying except me.

Why didn't I know. Why wasn't I told? The anger bubbled below the surface. At seventeen I was grown up enough to be left to care for her singlehandedly, to work out how to push morphine suppositories into her colostomy, to stay up all night most nights, taking catnaps on the sofa beside her bed, while my dad worked his regular night shift. At weekends when he wasn't working he never spent a night downstairs, but rather rolled in when

91

the pubs closed and he went straight to bed.

So I could do all that, but I wasn't adult enough to be told the truth. I felt so bad because once in the middle of the night when she was in agony she told me she wanted to die. I got angry with her and told her she couldn't give up, as me and my sister, Julie, needed her. So she had fought on and never mentioned it again. I feel guilty about this; instead of helping her pass peacefully by telling her we would miss her but would manage without her, I blackmailed her to carry on putting up with the pain, because no one told me she was dying.

I felt even more angry when I realised that even the district nurse, who came twice daily, and the Marie Curie nurse, who had just started doing two nights a week, couldn't face telling me the truth and brushed away my questions, even though I asked them frequently. So I presumed Mum was just going to carry on being frail, bedbound and ill. No one dies at forty-eight unless they're in a car crash, do they?

Looking back over the last few months it really was blatantly obvious. The sad look from the ladies at the chemist when I collected the morphine injections each week, who tentatively asked how she was doing. Well, the mystery of the plastic sheet was solved, that really was a cryptic clue. Two days before she died Mum stopped weeing; I told the district nurse when she called to give her a morphine injection.

"Well, her kidneys must have packed up. You need to put a plastic sheet over the mattress."

This was the nearest to a warning of impending death that I was given, but even this wasn't enough for me to grasp what was happening.

I spent hours pondering on how long you could live with "packed up kidneys." Perhaps they would burst into action again, hence the need for the plastic sheet, if that was what it was for. How was I supposed to get it on the mattress when she was bedbound? Where would I get one from? How could I fetch one when I couldn't leave her on her own? These were the questions of the day that never got asked or answered.

That was Friday. On Sunday night Dad had gone to the pub and me, my boyfriend, Pete, and my sister were watching TV with Mum. She suddenly started thrashing her arms and legs around, her teeth were clenched, and bubbles were coming out of her mouth. She didn't respond when I asked her what was wrong. It was scary to watch.

"Pete, take Julie next door,' I shouted.

I didn't want her to witness whatever it was that was happening, as she was only ten. Our lovely elderly neighbours, Mills and Walter, would look after her. I called the nurse, who came to the house. Though the thrashing had subsided, Mum still wouldn't talk to me.

"What's happening, nurse?"

She ignored the question and gave her the usual morphine injection. "Where is your dad? He should be here. I'll ask the doctor to come," was all she said as she practically ran for the front door.

So Pete went to get Dad. After he came home he took one look at Mum and asked Pete to fetch some beer from the shop across the road. After the beer arrived he sat in the kitchen with a glass and asked Pete to go out and round up the relatives. They duly arrived and after briefly looking at Mum joined him in the kitchen. The doctor came; he looked sad and patted everyone on the shoulder. He said something to Dad on the way out but I couldn't hear what it was.

Mum never woke up, and she died around midnight. Julie didn't know until the morning, as she was in bed next door.

The next few weeks were strange. I had so much time

on my hands even though I was back at work full time, did the cleaning, shopping, and washing. I worked in an office as the general dogsbody. Dad thought the family had gone up in the world, as a girl working in an office instead of the local knicker factory was really something special. Little did he know it was only a stop gap until I was eighteen and I could try to achieve my dream of being a student nurse. I had mentioned nurse training to my dad a few times but the response wasn't positive.

"Don't be stupid. Why would you want to leave your office job to work weekend and night shifts and deal with everyone's shit and blood?"

So I no longer mentioned it. Dad would always have the last word. But I could still have my dream.

*

At fourteen I'd had ambitious dreams after reading a careers book from the library, which my dad found rather amusing. I could see a world that stretched much further than the knicker factory. I was encouraged by my teachers to stay at school until sixteen and take CSEs. Most kids left school at fifteen to work in the local factories, as it wasn't a grammar school. Five grade one CSEs would allow access to A level work and if that was successful, university. So my career choices developed and got squashed in this order.

A vet! I loved animals. Dad's reaction to this couldn't have been any more shocked than if I had said I wanted to be the first woman to walk on the moon. There was no way he would support me through university, end of story.

So then I thought about being a veterinary nurse. You didn't need to go to university, or even do A-levels. However, you didn't really get paid for two years as it was a type of apprentice scheme. Dad said I needed to earn enough to keep myself and pay board. And anyway, I could possibly get bitten by a snake. (How cleverly he played on my fear of snakes.)

The next choice still related to animals. I would like to train to be a policewoman and eventually be a police dog handler. No need to stay at school, fair pay, and good prospects. I thought he would really like this idea. Wrong again. Dad had never been arrested but he was a bit Arthur Daly crossed with Del boy. He almost choked on his dinner when I presented my latest career ambition.

"For God's sake, have you lost your mind? Why can't you work in a factory like everyone else who leaves your school? What the hell would my friends think about me having a daughter who was a policewoman?"

So, one by one, my dreams were squashed, but thoughts on nursing gained momentum after Mum died. My precious career book also told me I could train as a nurse in the armed forces, so it was win-win. I would get to be a nurse and be able to see the world.

However, I also loved acting and always had a leading role in the school plays. After the last play of the term my English/Drama teacher actually suggested a career in the theatre. I got really excited because she told me that if I got three CSEs I could get to a college to study drama. You also did other general subjects such as English, maths, and other work related to theatre so it was still a useful thing to do. It could lead to all types of work. I didn't expect to be a famous film star, but you never know! I went home that day exuberant to say the least. I was sure Dad would love this idea because a teacher suggested it and if I did manage to become famous, then I would be earning lots of money.

What Dad thought about this career cannot be repeated here; needless to say dreams of being the next Judi Dench were well and truly squashed.

So I was back to nursing. I would need five grade one

CSEs to get into training, but I was prepared to work hard, and my teachers said I was more than capable. But Dad had always been against nursing; smart, nice girls worked in offices. So to be allowed to stay at school and take exams, I needed a plan B.

After a lot of pleading, begging, arguing, and an unwritten agreement that under no circumstances would I ask for money, I was allowed to stay the extra year. I had never asked for money, having started work as a papergirl at ten. At thirteen I was a Saturday shop assistant as well. Now, I saved what I could. The catch was that two of the subjects would be typing and office practice so I could get a job in an office.

But I had to leave school in the December having only done one term. I only returned to take the exams. This was when Mum had become very ill, gone into hospital, and had major surgery. So I stayed home to run the house and look after her and Julie. I was encouraged to study at home but it was only the Geography teacher that sent me any work to do and I didn't have a typewriter to practice on; however, the teachers still told me I would do okay.

Before the results came I had already decided that I was going to be a nurse and do training in the army or air force. I avidly watched MASH every week and imagined myself being Major Hot Lips Hoolahan.

By the time the results were due Mum was improving and taking over some of the housework, and I was working in an office. Life was relatively normal and I actually felt happy for a few weeks.

When the big scary envelope came I knew straightaway what it was. I didn't even hesitate, convinced by what the teachers had told me, and I ripped open the envelope. I had to read it over and over again before it sank in. Only one grade one. I cried and cried and no one in the family could see why I was so upset. I already had a job in an office so they thought results good or bad weren't relevant.

So I spent the next ten months working in the office. It was good to go to work and although the pay wasn't very good I still had my Saturday job as well and was saving up to have driving lessons when I was old enough. I hadn't given up on nursing altogether. I knew I could become a SEN without the CSEs, but that qualification wasn't recognised in other parts of the world, and even in England you would never be allowed to progress to be a district nurse or ward sister. I would apply anyway when I got a bit older, as you couldn't start training until you were eighteen. I wasn't giving up anytime soon.

Then, out of the blue Mum started to become ill again. It started quite subtly with tiredness, then she developed terrible pain, then the district nurse started coming to give morphine injections, the bed came downstairs, and I was in charge of the house again.

*

I really missed caring for Mum. In a strange way it had been very satisfying knowing that I had done as much as I possibly could to help keep her comfortable. Initially, I'd had doubts about a nursing career; what if I wasn't capable of dealing with some of the unsavoury nursing tasks and with seeing suffering and death? But Mum had left a legacy—me. I now knew that I could do it and was fired up, not only to be a nurse, but to be an exceptional one. I vowed I would never avoid questions from relatives and at some point in the future would be an exceptional district nurse and/or Marie Curie nurse.

After Mum died, I realised I couldn't leave home. I needed to support Julie, as I knew she would have a hell of a time with Dad if she was on her own with him.

But I could apply to the Nottingham School of Nursing to be an SEN or SRN and if needs be go to night school to get the required examinations. I discovered that the training required you to live in the nurse's home and do a three-month block of nights.

Two months after Mum died I went for an interview at the school of nursing. By this time, I knew it would be difficult, or even impossible, to leave home or do the night shifts. But I went anyway. I wasn't really nervous because I never thought I would be able to do it anyway. In retrospect it had been too close to Mum's death.

"Yvonne, nursing can be very stressful with patients suffering and dying. How do you know you'll be able to cope with this?" asked the rather overpowering lady behind the huge desk. I never even got further than, "Well, I looked after my mum until she died," before I started to blubber. This lady was the head of the school, Miss Finch; she was very kind when I cried. She was also very good at getting information out of you, but I managed to lie through my teeth and say yes to having lots of family support, and I didn't mention that Dad was working permanent nights and thought nurse training was the worst thing I could do.

Miss Finch was new to the post and was determined to sweep old traditions away and modernise nursing. She had already changed the uniforms to trousers. You no longer needed to live in the nursing home. Night shifts were now only one week per month, and you could take an IQ test if you hadn't got the relevant GCSEs/CSEs.

Whatever I said it must have been right.

"Yvonne, you have shown that even at your young age you seem to have what it takes to be a nurse. I would like to offer you a place on the SRN course if you can pass the IQ test. However, I must warn you it is very difficult," she said.

"When can I sit it?" I asked rather loudly as I was so fired up. I needed to know one way or another whether I could do this training or not. I sat the test that day. I managed to answer all the questions, so was floating on air as I left and started making my way to the bus stop. It could be up to two weeks before I would get the results. I decided I wouldn't mention the interview to Dad until I got the results.

"I had an interview last week to train as a registered nurse. I had to take an IQ test, which I passed, so I've been offered a place for May, 1972."

The silence was heavy, like a big black cloud filled the room. I was so happy that I had been offered a place. I just wanted someone to be proud of me and happy for me. It was teatime, and Dad glared across the table at me.

"I thought you'd dropped that stupid idea."

"Well, I haven't. I want to be a nurse. Mum said I would make a good nurse, so I'm going to do it."

"I thought you had to do nights."

"I do, but only one week a month."

'Well, who's going to look after Julie while you're on nights?"

At this point I was getting very het up; Julie was his daughter. Why should I have to be responsible for her? So the frustration just came out. Dad and I had endured many heated discussions, but I had never dared to shout at him. This time, instead of me thinking of a game plan, I just burst with anger and shouted, "Well, you'll have to change to days. You're always saying the boss would like you to do days." Looking at his red, angry face, I quickly regretted not thinking this through. I can honestly say I have never seen him so angry. As soon as we had finished eating and I had washed the pots, I made an excuse to go next door.

Mills and Walter had never had children so they doted

on me and Julie, and they were like loving grandparents, which Julie and I also lacked in our lives. There was always homemade cake; me and Julie spent a lot of time there when we wanted to escape from a father with an unpredictable temper. Mills knew straight away that I wasn't happy about something. So I told her all about the interview and IQ test and she was genuinely thrilled for me. I felt a bit of a traitor, and knew he would be even angrier, but I told her what Dad had said about having to look after Julie.

"What's the problem? Julie can always stay here when you're on nights," said Mills whilst giving me a hug.

I burst into tears. I was so grateful and touched by her kindness. Walter came in from his garden, we told him what had happened and he was also thrilled.

I left it a few days before mentioning the solution to Dad. Julie had said she didn't mind sleeping next door, so I put my brave pants on. "Dad, I think there is a way around me being able to train as a nurse without you having to give up working nights." I braced myself for the explosion, which turned out to only be medium sized.

"What brainwave have you come up with now? Are you going to make her sleep at the hospital or leave her on her own?" he asked gruffly.

"Neither. Mills and Walter are happy to have her stay there," I said a little too smugly.

"Well, aren't you the clever one, burdening old people just so you get to do what you want? Never mind us."

He was trying to send me on a guilt trip, but I wasn't going there, this was the most important decision of my life. "Well, yes, it is what I want to do. I really wanted to train in the army but moving away wouldn't be possible as you would need help even if you did work days. So I've decided to stay in Nottingham so that I can help look after Julie. Mills and Walter are more than happy to have Julie.

I love them, and I would never put on them, but Julie is happy to go there, so that's it. I'll be doing my training." After this monologue I stood back and watched his anger boil, but for once he didn't have an answer.

So I had nine months to plan for the start of the course. I had a list of things I needed to buy. A lot of books, a navy cardigan, and nurse's scissors. It doesn't sound a lot, but I had very little money left after paying board, but I managed it, including buying all the books. I was given a cardigan and scissors engraved with my name as a leaving present from the office staff.

I was given a list of the shift times for the hospital, as after the introductory six weeks I would be expected to work early and late shifts and could expect to work most weekends as well as night shifts after six months. It was then that I realised that there wasn't a bus that ran early enough to get me to work on time on Sundays. I dared not arrive late; I could get a bad report and be asked to leave the course, so I had nine months left to come up with a solution. There was no way I would be able to afford a taxi on a regular basis. I had passed my driving test, but had no funds to buy a car. Pete had a motorbike; I enjoyed riding pillion and had a helmet already. He suggested I bought a lightweight motorbike for myself. So I saved up as much as possible. A few weeks before the start of the course we went motorbike shopping. Pete helped me find a suitable one. I had a test drive and managed to stay on; I was going so slow, I'm sure a couple of pensioners on foot overtook me! The only problem was it cost eighty pounds and I only had thirty. There was no way I would ask Dad to lend me any money. I was under twenty-one so wasn't allowed to take out a loan agreement, but Dad seemed to have accepted that I was going to do the training and had been almost amiable at times. So I asked him if he would guarantee the loan for me.

Well…he wasn't being amiable with his reply. I think he actually enjoyed turning me down. Not to be beaten, I begged Pete to sign it for me. He wasn't happy in case his dominating mum found out, but he did it. So the following Saturday we fetched it. It was a Yamaha 50 and bright metallic orange. It looked brand new and very flashy. Dad was out having his lunch time session in the pub, so I parked it right outside the front door, complete with L plates, just to make sure he knew whose it was. He looked totally shocked, as he didn't know Pete was going to guarantee the loan for me.

But he was in a good mood and had a look at it and started it up. I even allowed him to ride it up and down the road. He genuinely seemed to like it. I was soon to find out why.

When he was due to leave for work on Monday night he actually had the nerve to say, "I might as well take your motorbike. It will do it good to have a run. It's not good for it to stand around not being ridden." He made it sound like he was doing me a favour.

"Well, if you had been kind enough to sign the loan agreement, then with pleasure I would have lent it to you. But as you had every reason not to help me, then I can promise you that you will never, ever borrow it."

With that, he wiped the rain off my push bike, which he had commandeered many years before and cycled off! I'm sure he must have felt very humiliated with his daughter having a motor bike and him only having a push bike. Although he tried on several occasions to talk me into lending it him, I stuck to my guns. Six weeks later he bought his own.

So in May, 1972 I started my training. I studied nearly every minute of my spare time. We only had exams towards the end of the course and I was determined I would pass them. We changed wards every nine weeks so I got experience in every speciality, and I loved them all. We had a report from each ward, and mine were always good. While it could be stressful, especially being in charge of a ward at night, I never regretted my career choice.

The three years flew by; I revised and revised and revised as the exams drew nearer. It was a three-hour exam in the morning and afternoon; I had already passed my four practical exams. Waiting for the results was the longest eight weeks of my life. I kept reliving the questions to the point where doubt crept in. At last the results arrived, and I could tell from the GNC logo on the envelope that this was it. I was really frightened to open it. What would Dad say when I failed? I dreaded to think. I had been on the end of his temper when my first two attempts at my driving test ended in failure; did he think I failed on purpose? After a few minutes of dithering I finally opened it.

I HAD PASSED.

Relief, tears, laughter, and every other emotion in between came out. There was no one at home to share my joy with and mobile phones hadn't yet been invented, so I immediately drove to see my friend, Liz. Had she passed? I was so annoyed when I arrived at her place; she was still fast asleep! Apparently she had been awake most of the night worrying and was now dead to the world. Really, she had probably had some alcohol to get her to sleep, as it took a jug of ice water carefully sprinkled on her face to get her conscious. I really wanted her to pass so we could celebrate together. The envelope sat there. Eventually, she was alert enough to realise why I was there. I held my breath while she opened the envelope. I was so full of joy but if my buddy and soul mate of three years had failed I would be nearly as devastated as her. But yes, she has passed as well. It was a Saturday, we had to work a late shift, but then we went out to celebrate. Saying I was overjoyed isn't enough to describe how I felt. I don't think I could have been any happier if I had won a million pounds on the lottery.

A few weeks later when we had our PIN numbers we were given staff nurse's uniforms. I even managed to get my dad to buy me a silver buckle. Did I feel good. I took a job on the burns and plastic surgery ward. I loved the work, helping patients coming to terms with their disfigurements. Two years later it was decided that they would separate the burns patients and have a separate burns unit. I was encouraged by the sister to apply for the sister's post. I got it and was the youngest sister to ever be appointed at that hospital. I was only twenty-three.

I worked there for three years and then somehow Miss Finch, who had interviewed me right at the beginning, heard about my work and asked me to do further training to become a nurse teacher. It would mainly be working with student nurses on the wards so I would still have contact with patients. The course I needed to do would be much more academic, which was a worry as I didn't even have a GCSE in English. But what an opportunity! I loved teaching the students on the unit and if I went into teaching I would be able to help turn out many more excellent, caring nurses. So I joined the school of nursing.

I travelled every day to Sheffield to do the teaching course and at the same time studied on my own to take part B of the London University Diploma in nursing. Very few nurses even managed to pass part A, but I had. I even had to have a viva in London, being questioned by a senior nurse and consultant surgeon. I passed everything and worked in the school of nursing for twenty years.

My dreams of being a district nurse had faded, but I was still committed to excellence in nursing care and ensured that my students were going to be competent and caring. However, there were changes taking place in education. I had to do a degree, which I did part time, and got a 2:1. This was because it was probable that we would be taken over by the university.

For the first two years after we became part of the university very little changed. But then it did with a bang. The courses became very academic, and students were judged on their ability to write an academic piece of work rather than on their nursing skills. I was spending so much time marking I had very little time to spend on the wards. I was missing being a nurse, and hated marking pieces of work on their academic merit rather than the content.

Then fate struck. I had started to teach on a post-registration course, and the participants were mainly district nurses and community staff nurses. I loved reading their case studies and listening to the class discussions about their patients. I think I was more than a bit jealous, and after each weekly session my thoughts would drift back to when the district nurses were attending Mum, and on my early wishes to become a district nurse. There were now staff nurses on the district; perhaps I could become one. Chatting to one of them I found out there was a part time post being advertised. It wasn't a popular area to work and the staff were getting desperate, and they even brought me an application form. But I was now a single parent with children and they needed support through university; I couldn't really afford the huge drop in pay, so I was sensible and didn't apply. A few weeks later they told me no one had applied and I was coerced into applying, being told there would be lots of opportunities for overtime.

So I applied and got the job. I also applied for the community evening service to supplement my income, and got that, somehow I managed but money was tight. But from the first day I knew it had been the right move. Even after all these years of nursing my enthusiasm had never waned. One day the sister took me to one side and told me how I was too good to be a staff nurse and she was going to recommend me for the district nursing course. If I completed that then I would be able to apply for sister's posts. I got on the course; it was another degree to be done in one year, and there were also placements. I loved the course and it gave me even more enthusiasm for district nursing. I passed with flying colours with a first class honours degree.

So I became a district nursing sister. I would have done this job without pay I loved it so much. I mentored my team and we were innovative in trying to prevent common problems such as leg ulcers and falls. We also instigated an early diagnosis and support project for dementia. Being passionate about the care of the dying, we were the first team to introduce the Macmillan gold standards for palliative care in our area. We had the privilege to care for many dying patients and their families, and the personal rewards were indescribable.

However, after ten years of being on the district, things had changed. New managers wanted every team to work the same way. I was told by one manager that our team was like Debenhams and the others were like Aldi; apparently we should lower our standards, rather than the other teams raise theirs. We did so much more than other teams because we worked harder and smarter. But to the manager it seemed we must be overstaffed, so my staffing levels were reduced despite having the same size caseload as the other teams. We also had to stop doing our "extras." Interestingly, a few years later the government were saying that the community staff should be an integral part of preventative and early diagnostic care.

So I'd finally had enough. Even after working many hours unpaid overtime each night and a lot of weekends, it was impossible to keep up standards. If I couldn't nurse patients properly and safely, I would leave. It was so bad

I could really see one of us ending up being struck off by the nursing council. After many arguments I took early retirement. I loved the job and was so sad to leave, but it was literally killing me. Money wasn't such an issue anymore. I now had a smaller house and the children had left home. However, I still needed to work to supplement my pension.

Fate struck again. I saw a job advertised for Nottinghamshire Hospice for the Hospice at Home team. This is the same type of job as the Marie Curie nurses who came at night to care for Mum. I applied and got the job. I've been here six years and love the work. We have a lovely boss, Jo, who started just after me. She is very proactive and when she found out I was a qualified nurse teacher she offered me teaching work as well. So I train our health care assistants as well as working nights. We're well supported and even appreciated by our managers, something that rarely happens in the NHS.

So forty-seven years after Mum died and forty-six years from when I started my nurse training, I have finally done everything I set out to do and more. Not only doing district nursing and hospice at home nursing, but also teaching and training many students and staff. I am still as enthusiastic as ever. I think I have done Mum proud. It was so sad she died so young, but I like to think it was for a reason; the reason being I could become and train excellent nurses. I am not the perfect nurse, but I always strive to be.

Dad mellowed somewhat as he got older. He even became proud of me and could be heard boasting, "My daughter's a Nurse Tutor."

There are a few lessons to take from this story. Firstly, never give up on your dreams. Turn them into reality. You can get there if you try hard enough.

Secondly, encourage and aid your children to follow their dreams. It's their career, not yours.

Lastly, always look after those who have looked after you. After my training I never saw much of Mills and Walter. I got married and moved a few miles away. I always meant to call but only managed it occasionally. I could have helped out much more when they were ill. It was only when I started district nursing that I realised they would have struggled to cope. It was much too late by then. Their support was pivotal in me becoming a nurse. For that I should have given back love and help when they became ill, but I didn't. I feel very guilty about that. That's why this story is dedicated to them.

Dedicated to my previous neighbours, Mills and Walter, and to my mum. In one way or another you made me who I am.

> Dear Yvonne
>
> I've had this card sat on my desk for months, trying to find the words to express how much you helped each of us through the worst period in our lives. Now I've realised that no words can do that and all I can say is 'Thank you' from the bottom of my heart. Without You we couldn't have made mums dream of going to Spain come true and those memories will last with us forever. I know my Mum would want me to thank you from her for looking after us, listening to us and supporting us.
> I hope you can go and treat yourself !!
> x x x

Over my years as a district nurse, my team and I
received lots of thank you cards and gifts.
But I remember this one so well because their
plight reminded me of my own mother's end of life
experience.I shared their journey with them.

Saturday Night Out with the Street Pastors
Margaret Parkes

9th September, 2017

It was the first time I'd taken my evening medication before going out for a "night on the town." I didn't factor my age (seventy-nine) into where I was going for the night. We met at the Malt Cross on St James Street at 9:45 p.m. Six street pastors, Joan Dwane, and myself. Joan and I were only there for observation. We were joined by two policewomen for the briefing before going out. The pastors are all first aid trained and always carry with them a large first aid bag and a pack containing bottle of water, flip flops, and plenty of lollipops. Some people think street pastors are only there to help the homeless, but they're actually there to help if anyone gets injured, or is intoxicated, or simply need someone to talk to. I joined them because I wanted the experience.

The pastors are in phone contact with the police and also use camera surveillance in the city centre. I'm assuming that's because the pastors are vulnerable too. The leader said a short prayer before we went out in two groups of four. The street pastors knew all the people sleeping on the streets by their first names. They were asking how they were and giving out water and lollipops. They also have phone numbers they can give out if anyone needs help or advice.

Groups of girls stopped to talk to us as we were all wearing jackets with "Street Pastors" written on them. One lady said she was over from Ireland and they didn't have anything like that over there. They were all dressed up (something I noticed since I was rag trade for so many years) but they still took the time to stop and ask, which was nice. All the bouncers on the doors of the pubs and clubs, and even the drivers of the police vans, waved and called hello. We were even stopped and blessed by a group of men out on a stag night dressed as vicars. I'm a naturally sociable person, so I really liked that aspect. It was a bustling atmosphere, but it's changed quite a bit from when I was a teenager. There used to be more of a pub atmosphere filled with people of all ages. Now it seems like a mostly young crowd and there are bouncers on the doors.

Waves of nostalgia swept over me as we walked along the streets in the Lace Market. The large black gates of 10 Fletcher Gate are still there. It is almost sixty-five years since I walked through them for my first day of work at fifteen years of age as a trainee sewing machinist.

I worked from eight a.m. to six p.m. and I was paid £2 a week less two shillings and nine old pence for National Insurance. Take home pay was £1.73. The year was 1953. Coronation year. The firm of Brownwood and Clarke no longer exists; it's now a Tesco Express.

The street pastors took a break at twelve thirty. I'd had a sleep in the afternoon, so I was still feeling all right. We queued up at McDonald's and took it back to the Malt Cross. One group was then called out to Clumber Street to see a lady having problems and our group was asked by the police to go to one of the pubs to see a lady who was intoxicated. When we went in she was at the bar, and a gentleman was talking to her. The street pastors spoke to her for some time before putting her in a safe taxi home. The gentleman who'd been talking to her came over to say he'd been worried about her because he had daughters that age. I was so glad that someone was there to help her.

While they were walking around the streets, the police had asked if the pastors would pick up the empty glass bottles and dispose of them in the rubbish bins as people were getting injured on broken glass.

We went back to the Malt Cross at 2:50 a.m. They said it had been a quiet night, as the university students weren't yet back. The mind boggles at the thought of dealing with so many more people on a night out! We finished with a prayer before going home. Bed at 4:15 a.m. after a very interesting and satisfying night.

PS: We never did see any of the ladies from Trent Valley Ladies Probus, who said they would be coming into town to cause "mayhem."

The Day My Life Began
Raymond Mellors

I was about fifteen or sixteen and I used to go to the cinema with my mate. One night we were queuing up at the Vernon Picture House in Basford, and I saw these two young ladies. I knew one of them but not the other, and I said to my mate, "That one's mine," pointing out the young lady I didn't know. She looked lovely in my opinion; she really struck me with her dark, neck length hair and blue eyes, and you could tell that she took pride in her appearance.

So when they came down the queue I said to them, "We'll save you a couple of seats," which we did. Then, when they came down the aisle I stood up, like the gentleman I am, and I made sure that I let the other girl I knew go past me and sat this young lady next to me. So as the evening went on we got chatting, as you do, and I found out that her name was Doris and that she worked at Player's (the big cigarette manufacturer back then). I also worked at Player's.

When the show finished I asked, "Where do you live?" and she said, "Aspley." We were in Basford and this was a couple of miles away, but I walked her all the way home. I can't remember whether I kissed her, but we said goodnight and I did say to her, "I'll see you tomorrow night."

Her mum was there. "No, you won't!" she shouted up to me.

"Why not?" I asked.

"Because she's got housework to do," her mum replied.

So I came over and helped her with the housework that day, just so I could spend time with her.

Anyway, we used to go to the picture house a lot, maybe twice a week. Sometimes we went to the Forum, opposite where she lived, and on one occasion I arranged to meet her there. This was quite a long way from where I lived and I didn't really know the area. I had to walk right down Melbourne Road, through the Aspley Estate. Being a stranger to the area I once got lost and had to ask a fella coming down the hill how to get out of the estate.

"You go up there and through the twitchell and it's just the other side of the road," he said.

So I did that but I was about half an hour late by then and expected Doris not to be there anymore. But there she was, standing in the foyer. I thought to myself, "My luck is in tonight." We used to get two tickets for the balcony, right at the back in the corner—to this day I couldn't tell you what any of the films were about. We always had the same seats, and sometimes it was like they still felt warm from the last time we'd been there! When they came to knock the Forum down, we went to see if we could rescue the seats we sat in as we wanted to have them in the house, but they had been demolished along with the building.

I was around sixteen when I met her, and when I was eighteen, the National Service snatched me up and I went to Lincoln for infantry training, and then on to Dover in the Grand Barracks. I can remember one night going out to the cinema in Dover with my mate who was also in the Yorkshire and Lincolnshire regiment and there was the most terrific bang.

"That was a shell!" I said. We went out to see what was happening, and do you know, not a single person in the cinema moved from watching the film. All of the "civvies" sat still and there we were, two soldiers, panicking away! We went down to the barracks and climbed up the tower to watch them shelling the convoy in the channel from the French coast. You could see all the flashes and bombs falling in the night which stopped when the convoy had gone passed.

When I was about twenty, I had some Christmas leave to take over December and January.

"I'm coming home, shall we get married then?" I asked Doris.

That was as much of a proposal as it was, and when I got home she'd got the cake and dress all ready. In those days you had to use coupons to get everything, and you'd need a lot of coupons for a wedding dress, so a friend of hers said that she could borrow her wedding dress, and that's what she did.

And so we were married, and after a few days I said to her, "Now that we're married, if anything happens to me you'll get a pension." And my wife swiped me across the face; I can still feel it now! She wasn't pleased with the suggestion that anything would happen to me.

I did go back, and I was one of many who crossed over the Rhine. But I came home and we had a very happy marriage. I enjoyed every moment of our fifty-three years together, and it wasn't long enough for me. We got on really well together and had two beautiful daughters, and they're looking after me now. Doris worked in the hospital, and when she died she passed away on the same ward she'd worked on for so many years.

A Little Boy
Jacob Lee

It's my space to reconnect and go within. A daily practice to be and radiate Love.

The crisp cold air rushes over my face as I lay on the edge of the moss covered pontoon, the mirror-clear body of water beneath me. Dangling my arms over the side, just touching the water with the very edge of my fingertips.

I lay there looking in silence. Watching the ripples expand until I no longer see them. I am embraced by calmness, stillness, a warmth I haven't felt for a very long time.

I stare for what seems like an eternity, looking at the reflection of this man looking back at me. I don't recognise him. He looks like me, but I cannot feel him.

*

I open my eyes for the first time, realising I am in A&E drifting in and out of consciousness. I feel such pain. *Why am I here?* This is not where I want to be. *Why?*

Sitting up for the first time like a new-born looking at his world in wonderment and awe. Not being able to stand, knowing my trunk will not carry this frame.

I just sit and feel my way around looking for something to grab hold of that feels familiar. It's not there though. A fear like no other. I surrender.

*

Stood at the edge, looking out over the mirror of water in front of me. Tears cascading down my face. My heart isn't beating. It is just still, holding me there whilst I feel this, in all its beauty. Pain.

I take a deep breath inwards and begin to fall forward. Like someone has me on a remote control and frame by frame I fall towards the reflection of this man before me.

The coldness of the water doesn't take my breath away. I sense no temperature, just a stillness and silence unlike anything I have ever experienced.

I see laying on the floor of the lake, a shape; I cannot make it out. As hard as I can, I kick, and kick, and I reach out.

As I reach this figure my vision clears, and I see there a little boy, just curled up, naked as though he were laying in a crib.

I feel myself being drawn back to the surface…No!

With all my strength, with all my heart, I reach out with both my hands and grab this beautiful little boy and hold him tightly against my chest. We both spiral upwards like a flower opening to the rays of the sunshine in the morning light.

My eyes open and we are sat on the edge of the lake. And this little face looks up at me and says, *I found you, I have finally found you.* He was taken all those years ago by a beautiful soul I could not fend off.

"A beautiful soul," you may ask?

I can now look at your face and let you feel the strength of the love within me. What you took from me, I now take back. I will not remain in the darkness with you. As part of my own acceptance I surround you with my light and love.

That is my gift to you.

I cannot begin to explain in words the feeling that rushed through my core. To lose the boy all those years ago, and to now hold him in my arms.

*

*

My journey moving forward will be scary and will be full of fearful experiences. There will be times where I question my role on this little rock.

A beginning, an understanding that what I seek is within me and has always been within me.

Together now we can shine as bright as the love I feel in my soul.

Those hearts I've touched caught mine as I fell.

Traffic Lights
Janice Dent

It's true what they say about volunteering; you get back so much more than you give. I hadn't imagined how wonderful it could be making tea and toast for the day therapy patients at the Hospice. We have a giggle and do the activities together, which is what has brought me to this page. Global Wordsmiths came along and gave us all the opportunity to tell stories about different aspects of our lives. What I get up to outside of the Hospice may surprise a few here, but this is my story.

The first time it happened I was about eight. I was travelling in the family car.

In the back, my brother and I had designated sides, our territory defined by the leatherette arm rest which was always put down firmly between us, lest either should inadvertently sprawl beyond our jurisdiction. So my view was the familiar one of the back of my mother's head. I was always secretly glad to be the one behind her, out of her field of vision and the scope of her judgmental eye. Car trips could get tetchy, so safest out of view.

The familiar profile of my dad was behind the driver's seat, eyes front, concentrating on the traffic, keeping us all safe. And my lovely brother to my right, two years my elder, quiet and thoughtful, holding his packet of polo mints prescribed by my mother to stave off his travel sickness.

I was bored. The mood was dreary, the weather was dreary, and the car slowed to a halt at a traffic light. The engine idled. I gazed mindlessly out of the window. And that's when it happened.

Suddenly and quite unexpectedly, I found myself out of my body, floating over the clock tower of the building opposite. I was looking down at our grey Triumph 2000, sitting at the traffic lights with us in it. I felt slightly alarmed, but the floating sensation wasn't unpleasant. I felt sort of spacious and I remember trying to make sense of this strange turn of events. Then, as I looked down, I thought, *What if the traffic lights change to green?* Gripped with sudden panic that I would be left behind, abandoned forty feet above a road junction, I snapped back into my body. Wide eyed and heart thumping, I was back in my seat.

I looked furtively at the backs of Mum and Dad, terrified I'd be in trouble, but strangely they didn't seem to have noticed. I remember pushing my head as far back as possible into the car seat so that I could swivel just my eyes to look at my brother. Had he noticed my absence? Apparently not. He was just as I'd left him. I seemed to have got away with it. If Mum knew, I would've been in big trouble. Big trouble for getting out of the car, ridiculed for talking nonsense, chastised for making things up. There was nothing to be gained from mentioning it. So I didn't.

I just sat there, slightly awestruck and rooted to my grey leatherette seat. To my eight-year-old self, it was a mysterious secret.

And so began a series of similar episodes of "leaving my body" and floating above it. Usually in school assemblies or lessons which were so tedious that I'd go a bit dreamy…and *whoosh*, up I'd go. But I never mentioned it to anyone. I assumed such things were taboo, like so much about the mysteries of life, which the fear of ridicule had taught me not to mention or ask about.

Me daydreaming in 1972

As my teens passed in a messy blur of exams, awkwardness, blue eyeshadow, and self-discovery, I'd almost forgotten this childhood phenomenon. Until aged nineteen, and I found myself at university.

I wasn't quite sure how I'd got there. We were working class stock. It wasn't expected and I'd never really *wanted* to go. I had no interest in the Chemistry and Pharmacology I was studying, but in the absence of a better plan and with the school's presumption that "that's what clever girls do," there I was. A square peg in a round hole sitting in an Organic Chemistry lecture with about a hundred other 1980's students.

I was frantically scribbling notes, trying to keep up with something I didn't understand or even care about, until finally a wave of futility swept over me and I put down my pen. Defeated.

I leaned back and surveyed the sea of woolly jumpers and unwashed hair that stretched out before me in a hormonal fug. I wondered how many of these other students really wanted to be here? Was it really just me who didn't?

I gazed down at the professor, droning on, a caricature in brown corduroy. *Jeez, this is so tedious and pointless. Is this really what my life is all about?*

And then, like all those years before, I was suddenly out of my body again, looking down at my despairing self, sat on the curved, terraced seating of the lecture theatre. I was in that same detached, floaty void and felt the same mild alarm. But this time it was different. I wasn't alone. To my left I suddenly felt the presence of a fatherly old man and he spoke to me.

"It's okay," he said. "You can leave. You can go. Everything will be all right."

I snapped back into my body. I sat perfectly still, trying to make some sense of what had just happened. All I knew was that I was profoundly touched that this man seemed to understand my plight and I was deeply comforted. I was so convinced of his support for me that I picked up my pen and drew a horizontal line under my notes and beneath that line, in capitals letters, I wrote THE END.

I sat through the remainder of the lecture in complete confidence that despite the uncertainty of what the future would hold, I would leave university that day and everything would be all right. I had never felt more sure of anything in my life.

I made an excuse to avoid lunch with my friends, and with that, I walked home, stuffed my belongings into my rucksack, and without a word to anyone, walked to the coach station and boarded a National Express to my future.

That future unfolded into the familiar tapestry of life experience. Working hard, seeing the best and worst of humanity, love, death, struggle, loss, triumph, facing fears, finding joy, and three beautiful children. And those twenty-five years completely papered over the memory of those strange out of body experiences of my youth.

So at forty-four, and in the calmer waters which followed the storm of my life, I knew I needed to stop, reflect, and take stock. I looked at the leaflet next to the computer on my desk. It had been there a while. It looked back at me.

Meditation Class, Weds Evenings 7-9pm, South Notts College.

"A Scandinavian method based on western psychological and scientific understandings." I could cope with that. I'd worked in a pharmaceutical laboratory and in property renovation, and I wasn't interested in any spiritual hippy nonsense.

So I went. There were sixteen of us. A motley assortment in a Portakabin with fuzzy grey carpet tiles, our exploits illuminated by unforgiving fluorescent strip-lights overhead. What could be so hard about sitting with your eyes closed for half an hour? We bonded and laughed over the trials and tribulations of an activity which sounded so simple but transpired to be anything but, as we explored our inner landscapes together.

And then one evening in a beautiful, nostalgic bolt of wonderment, on a blue plastic chair in a Portakabin, I slipped into that long forgotten out of body void I hadn't visited since that Chemistry lecture in 1982. I was as awestruck as that girl at the traffic lights in 1972. It was like a homecoming.

Wikipedia:
"Astral projection (or astral travel) is a term used in esotericism to describe a willful out of body experience that assumes the existence of a soul or consciousness called the astral body that is separate from the physical body and capable of travelling outside it throughout the universe. The idea of astral travel is ancient and occurs in multiple cultures. There is no scientific evidence that there is a soul or consciousness separate from normal neural activity or one that can consciously leave the body and make observations."

The next ten years of my life were an exploration of the scientifically unproven.

My daily meditation continued. It was the spaces between the thoughts, not the thoughts themselves, which lured me and I accessed my void at will. Somehow I felt connected to something greater than that which we all subscribe to. A different, higher level of 'flow', but for which I had no words to adequately describe. My hands would get hot and the whole experience felt energetic. Long forgotten memories resurfaced complete with the emotional intensity I'd felt at the time. It was quite disconcerting.

My meditation teacher could offer no insight. The class eventually wound up when she returned to Norway and I was on my own.

I confided about my funny meditations to an old school friend over a coffee one day.

"You should try Reiki, Janice," he said. "That'd be right up your street, that's all energy and stuff."

I'd never heard of it.

My ego resisted violently as I googled Reiki. "New age hippy rubbish," it chided. It took some courage to sign up to a weekend course and sit there imagining balls of energy and columns of light, but I did it.

And I learnt that we have a human energy field. Energy pathways that run through our physical, emotional, mental, and spiritual bodies, and that these all interconnect. And that we can channel energy that is all around us to enhance our own energy fields, promoting better health.

So it dawned on me that I had been inadvertently channeling energy and self-healing all this time. Clearing out emotional blockages, releasing old traumas. The baggage large and small of the last forty-five years began to transform. And I'd never felt so good.

Reiki was in the right ball park, but I knew it still wasn't exactly "it." So I carried on undaunted with my energetic version of meditation, until one evening when I cleared out an experience so traumatic and confusing that I was at a total loss.

In my void I was a man in a damp, drizzly field in medieval times. I was ambushed by two men in long tunics who speared me through the chest with a broken tree branch, and I experienced what could only be described as a hideous and terrifying death, drowning as my lungs filled with blood. I relived it in graphic visual and emotional detail. Afterwards, I collapsed onto my bed, quaking and spent, panting and rocking in the foetal position. My eyes were on stalks. What the hell was that?

"How long 'til dinner, Mum?" came a cry from the other side of the door. And I was back in my more usual reality.

This was bonkers. I was put in touch with a spiritual teacher by the Reiki lady. He phoned me and explained that I had experienced a death from a previous life and suggested that I might want to come and see him. Adrift in a world now way beyond my understanding, I agreed.

And so I found myself sat cross legged on a big floor cushion, trying to disguise how painful it was, as I hadn't sat cross legged since I was about six. There was a big, purple amethyst to my right, some rainbow-coloured pictures adorning the walls, and relaxing bongy music in the back ground. I was anything but relaxed. I was like a rabbit in headlights. *What am I doing here?* I didn't say a thing. Yet I was sat opposite a slight man in his sixties who seemed, reassuringly, to know what was going on with me. He smiled kindly over his glasses and told me I was very brave. He said one day I would be sitting opposite people this way, only I would be the one doing the talking. He smiled again at my blank and clueless expression. He said I was a spiritual healer in the making. I didn't have a clue what he was talking about.

With his help and guidance over the coming years, my opening up accelerated and I learnt a new language. That of the scientifically unproven spiritual world.

As in the chemistry lecture all those years ago, I started encountering other non-physical beings in my void. A Mongolian guide; my late father and other spirits; dead people who passed on messages in mirror writing (which explained another childhood peculiarity—a compulsion to write reams in mirror writing). I encountered cheeky monkey spirits just messing around, as well as more malevolent entities. I didn't know what the point of all this was but I trusted my teacher, who said that I was just passing through all this and not to worry, that I was headed beyond it. He didn't say where to and I didn't ask. It felt important so I just carried on.

The rest of life rolled on, too. My eldest children left for university, and I had a new part-time job in a shop, but I only told a trusted few open-minded friends about the goings-on on my meditation chair after making the lunch boxes and washing up every night.

My teacher said I had a powerful psychic presence. I felt too silly to actually ask what that was. I would make mental notes of many things he said and then Google them at home.

I then found that I only had to *think* of another person and I was in their energy field. Without them being physically there, I could bring energy into them in the same way as I could bring it into myself. My hands moved around and as the energy pushed through blockages in their auras, I felt the emotions coming out associated with their traumas which had caused the congestion. Just as I had with my own. I was now crying out other people's grief, terror, and shame and experiencing every nuance of their emotional pain as it passed harmlessly through me. Sometimes I would get vignettes, as I called them; visual pictures and other information about what was going on during the trauma.

With experience and understanding I gathered confidence, and gradually started working directly with people. It felt like a big responsibility. It was profoundly moving. It was healing.

Along the way I learnt about other realms beyond the awareness of most. I was introduced to angels and visited a space of timeless love where we exist beyond the constraints of our physical form. I learnt about past life phenomena and all of it was beautiful and humbling.

I knew there were spirit healing guides working through me doing this work. I had encountered enough spirits by then. And besides, I had seen them. An older man and two women, Native American shamanic healers. Their personalities are now very familiar. I like them. All three work together through me now like a team, clearing out energetic debris and stagnation, making the energy flow healthier and returning lost and fragmented soul parts to gradually make people more whole.

A person ultimately heals themselves, and their own higher consciousness will take what they need for their highest good. I know I am only a channel for this energy. It is not for the faint hearted. It can be an emotional ride as energies are stirred up, sorted out, and settle into the new energetic framework. Healing hurts. But it is short lived and worth it as new ways, free of old limiting patterns, become possible.

And now, as my spiritual teacher predicted, I sit opposite people and talk to them, calling my guides in to help them. I support them on their journey. I know it's what I'm here for. It's my purpose and I am truly grateful.

That's my story of becoming a spiritual trance healer. So if you're sat at the traffic lights and notice your child on the roof opposite, don't be too quick to tell them off.

Love,
Janice

With special thanks to:

nottinghamshire hospice
adding life to days

The Arts Council England

Supported using public funding by

ARTS COUNCIL ENGLAND

LOTTERY FUNDED

What's Your Story?

Global Wordsmiths, CIC, provides an all-encompassing service for all writers, ranging from basic proofreading and cover design to development editing, typesetting, and eBook services.

Our education and cultural programme offers a wide range of services for all ages, including writing and photography workshops designed to suit the current curriculum, as well as a range of publishing packages from concept and design through to publication.

A major part of our work is charity and community focused, delivering writing projects to under-served and under-represented groups across Nottinghamshire, giving voice to the voiceless and visibility to the unseen.

To learn more about our work visit: www.globalwords.co.uk

Other books by Global Words Press:

Defining Moments: Stories from a Place of Recovery
World at War: Farmilo Primary School, Year Six
Making Headway: Living with Brain Injury
Women's Stories, Women's Voices
The Victorian Vale: Farmilo Primary School, Year Six
Times Past: Young at Heart
In Different Shoes: Stories of Trans Lives
Patriotic Voices: Stories of Service
From Surviving to Thriving: Reclaiming Our Voices
Fractured Voices: Breaking the Silence
Don't Look Back, You're Not Going That Way
Peace by Piece
Speaking OUT: LGBTQ Youth Memoirs
Late OutBursts: LGBTQ Memoirs